Barefoot Island

THEODORE CLYMER
RICHARD L. VENEZKY
ROSELMINA INDRISANO

Consultants
CLAIRE HENRY
DALE D. JOHNSON
HUGHES MOIR
P. DAVID PEARSON
PHYLLIS WEAVER

Ginn and Company

0-663-38985-2

Acknowledgments: Grateful acknowledgment is made to the
following publishers, authors, and agents for permission to
use and adapt copyrighted material:

Atheneum Publishers, Inc., for "The Story of Pepe the
Clown," adapted from *My Great-Grandfather, the Heroes
and I* by James Krüss. Copyright © 1973 by Atheneum
Publishers, Inc. Reprinted by permission of the publisher.
Also for "Dead End Bluff," adapted from *Dead End Bluff* by
Elizabeth Witheridge. Copyright © 1966 by Elizabeth
Witheridge. Reprinted by permission of Atheneum
Publishers.

The Dial Press for "Last Days of Brightness," Parts 1 and
2, by David Budbill. Adapted from *Snowshoe Trek to Otter
River* by David Budbill. Copyright © 1976 by David Budbill.
Reprinted by permission of The Dial Press. Also for "Yagua
Days" by Cruz Martel. Adapted from *Yagua Days* by Cruz
Martel. Text copyright © 1976 by Cruz Martel. Reprinted by
permission of The Dial Press.

Dodd, Mead & Company, Inc., for the text, with
illustrations, of *Blue Moose* by Manus Pinkwater. Reprinted
by permission of Dodd, Mead & Company, Inc. Copyright ©
1975 by Manus Pinkwater.

Doubleday & Company, Inc., for the poem "If Once You
Have Slept on an Island" by Rachel Field from her book *Taxis
and Toadstools*, Copyright 1926 by the Century Company.
Reprinted by permission of Doubleday & Company, Inc., and
of World's Work Ltd, publishers in the United Kingdom and
British Commonwealth.

Elsevier-Dutton Publishing Co., Inc., for "So You Want
to Write Bad Jokes!" from *Jokes to Read in the Dark* by Scott
Corbett. Copyright © 1980 by Scott Corbett. Reprinted by
permission of the publisher, E. P. Dutton. Also for "Jim
Bridger's Alarm Clock," adapted from *Jim Bridger's Alarm
Clock and Other Tall Tales* by Sid Fleischman. Text
copyright © 1978 by Sid Fleischman. Illustrations copyright
© 1978 by Eric von Schmidt. Reprinted by permission of the
publisher, E. P. Dutton.

Elsevier/Nelson Books for "Encyclopedia Brown: The
Case of the Wanted Man" by Donald J. Sobol. Reprinted by
permission of Elsevier/Nelson Books. Adapted, with
solution, from the book *Encyclopedia Brown Keeps the
Peace* by Donald J. Sobol. Copyright © 1969 by Donald J.
Sobol.

Harcourt Brace Jovanovich, Inc., for the poem "Buffalo
Dusk" from *Smoke and Steel* by Carl Sandburg, copyright
1920 by Harcourt Brace Jovanovich, Inc.; copyright 1948 by
Carl Sandburg. Reprinted by permission of the publisher.

Harper & Row, Publishers, Inc., for an adaptation of the
text of "The Steadfast Tin Soldier" from *Seven Tales* by Hans
Christian Andersen, translated by Eva LeGallienne. Text ©
1959 by Eva LeGallienne. By permission of Harper & Row,
Publishers, Inc. Also for the text of "Sam", Chapter 1, *The
Trumpet of the Swan* by E. B. White. Text copyright © 1970 by
E. B. White. By permission of Harper & Row, Publishers, Inc.
Also for "Prairie Winter," Parts 1 and 2, a text excerpt from

The Long Winter by Laura Ingalls Wilder. Copyright, 1940, as
to text, by Laura Ingalls Wilder. Renewed, 1968, by Roger L.
MacBride. By permission of Harper & Row, Publishers, Inc.

Houghton Mifflin Company for the lines from "A Song of
Greatness" on page 172. From *The Children Sing in the Far
West* by Mary Austin, published by Houghton Mifflin
Company. Copyright 1928, by Mary Austin. Reprinted by
permission of the publisher.

Houghton Mifflin/Clarion Books for "The Foundling,"
slightly adapted from *The Foundling* by Carol Carrick.
Copyright © 1977 by the author, and reprinted by permission
of Houghton Mifflin/Clarion Books, New York.

Little, Brown and Company for "The Fire Bringer" by
Margaret Hodges. Adapted from *The Fire Bringer: A Paiute
Indian Legend* retold by Margaret Hodges. Copyright © 1972
by Margaret Hodges. By permission of Little, Brown and
Company.

Random House, Inc., for "The Skates of Uncle Richard"
by Carol Fenner. Adapted by permission of Random House,
Inc. from *The Skates of Uncle Richard*, by Carol Fenner.
Copyright © 1978 by Carol Fenner Williams. Also for "A
Thousand Pails of Water" by Ronald Roy. Adapted by
permission of Alfred A. Knopf, Inc. from *A Thousand Pails of
Water*, by Ronald Roy. Copyright © 1978 by Ronald Roy. Also
for "Christopher Columbus" by Piero Ventura. Adapted by
permission of Random House, Inc. from *Christopher
Columbus*, by Piero Ventura, based on the text by Cian Paolo
Cesarani. Copyright © 1978 by Random House, Inc. Also for
"Welcome to Troy!" by Gerald Gottlieb. Adapted by
permission of Random House, Inc. from *The Adventures of
Ulysses*, by Gerald Gottlieb. Copyright © 1959 by Gerald
Gottlieb.

Charles Scribner's Sons for the poem "Your Own Best
Secret Place" from *Your Own Best Secret Place* by Byrd
Baylor. Text copyright © 1979 by Byrd Baylor. Reprinted by
permission of Charles Scribner's Sons.

Simon & Schuster for "Perplexing Puzzles and
Tantalizing Teasers," with solutions, from *Perplexing
Puzzles and Tantalizing Teasers* by Martin Gardner,
illustrated by Laszlo Kubinyi. Text copyright © 1969 by
Martin Gardner. Illustrations copyright © 1969 by Laszlo
Kubinyi. Reprinted by permission of Simon & Schuster, a
Division of Gulf & Western Corporation.

Viking Penguin Inc. for the adaptation "Will's Quill," with
selected illustrations, from *Will's Quill* by Don Freeman.
Copyright © 1975 by Don Freeman. Reprinted by permission
of Viking Penguin Inc. Also for the adaptation "Pippi Finds a
Spink" from *Pippi in the South Seas* by Astrid Lindgren.
Copyright © 1957 by Astrid Lindgren. Reprinted by
permission of Viking Penguin Inc.

Frederick Warne and Co., Inc., New York, for "My Island
Grandma" by Kathryn Lasky. Adapted from *My Island
Grandma* copyright © Kathryn Lasky 1979. Reprinted by
permission of the publisher, Frederick Warne and Co., Inc.

George Allen & Unwin (Publishers) Ltd., England, for
"The Wild Geese" by Tsumori Kunimoto from *Japanese
Poetry: the "Uta"* by Arthur Waley. Reprinted by permission
of the publisher.

Margaret Baker, England, for her story "Rhyming Ink,"
adapted from *Fifteen Tales for Lively Children* by Margaret
and Mary Baker. Published by Dodd, Mead & Co. Used by
permission of the author.

Bill Berger Associates, Inc., for "Jim Bridger's Alarm
Clock," adapted from *Jim Bridger's Alarm Clock and Other*

(Continued on page 478)

CONTENTS

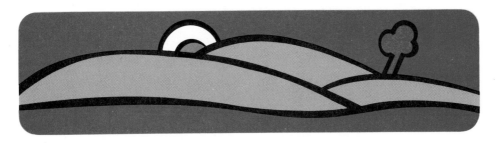

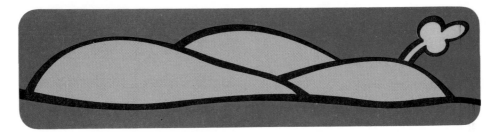

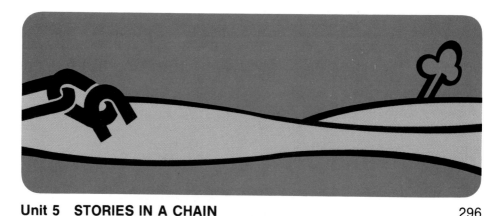

Have you ever thought about why people smile?
Friends smile because they are glad to be friends. Clowns
smile to make others happy, and children smile when they
discover something new.

Some people say that even the moon is smiling. Take a
look and see if you agree.

at the Moon

Quig often thought about Dead End Bluff. When he had to deal with the bluff, the situation was more than he counted on.

DEAD END BLUFF

ELIZABETH WITHERIDGE

Quig loved to fish where the small river cut its channel out into the big one. This evening his family was having a picnic with some friends. Quig caught several plump sunfish and thought of the night in June when he cast and came up with his dog, Storm, on his hook.

"Luckiest accident I ever had," Quig said, feeling around for the dog. Storm always tried to keep at a safe distance from his rod now, but he did enjoy being close to Quig.

Tommy, Quig's younger brother, was dredging along the edge of the river with a minnow net. He was

11

collecting frogs. He kept the frogs in an old dishpan in the backyard. They were mostly little green speckled things, but Tommy hoped one day to catch the "big old bullfrog" that lived below Dead End Bluff. He made lots of trips to the bottom of the bluff in the daytime, but never saw the bullfrog. "Quig's right. I'll have to go at night, I guess," said Tommy. "That's when we always hear him. I guess I'll go tonight."

"Oh, no, you won't go down to Dead End tonight or any other night!" exclaimed his mother.

"Imagine going down there in the dark!" said Quig's friend Peggy.

Quig smiled to himself and thought that it would be just as easy for him to go down the bluff at night as it would in the daytime. Even though Quig was blind, he still had a sense of humor.

The night after the picnic, Quig's parents went with the Munsons and the Bradfords to have dinner in Green Valley. Quig and Peggy had been elected to sit with the three younger children and the dogs. Quig and Peggy were listening to records on the front porch while Tommy, Pete, and Marcy were playing in the backyard.

"I don't hear the kids," Quig said abruptly. "We'd better look for them."

Peggy put on a record. "Oh, they're all right. I checked on them just a few minutes ago. Listen to this."

"That's great," said Quig, "but turn it off a minute, will you, Peg?"

He walked down off the porch and stood listening.

"Tommy," he shouted. "Tom, where are you?"

No answer.

"Let's go," said Quig, coming back to the porch for his cane.

Peggy shut off the record player and followed him down the walk.

"Where shall we look?" she asked, hurrying to keep up with his long strides. "They certainly aren't far away. It can't be more than ten minutes since I saw them."

Quig was tapping his cane along the sidewalk toward Dead End Bluff.

"I think we'd better go to Dead End first. I've a feeling my little brother has some business there. Is it dark yet, Peg?"

"Not quite," replied Peggy. "It's only 8:30. It's just kind of dusk. It would be dark at the bottom of Dead End, though. What would Tommy be doing on Dead End Bluff in the dark, Quig?" Suddenly there was panic in her voice. "Oh, no, they couldn't be there!"

"I think they could," Quig insisted. "We'll have to see." As he spoke, they could hear the big old bullfrog somewhere below the bluff.

"Tommy," he called again. They were almost at the end of the road now. "Tommy, are you down there?"

This time he heard voices, all jumbled together. Then Tommy's voice: "I'm down here, Quig. I'm hunting my frog, but I don't want Pete and Marcy to come down. Make them go back. They don't know all about the bluff the way I do."

"Tom Smith," Quig commanded sternly, "you come back up that bluff this minute, do you hear? Pete and Marcy, you come back immediately!"

"We're coming, Quig," Pete said. "We went only halfway down. We're coming right up."

Quig heard them puffing and the sound of their feet scrambling on the rock steps. In a minute they were at the top. Peggy pulled them up over the top.

"Tommy," Quig shouted, "if you aren't on your way up by the time I count to ten, I'm coming down after you."

"Ho, ho!" laughed Tommy at the bottom of the bluff. "You've never been down Dead End in your life. Daddy won't let you. I'm going to stay down here till I get my big old frog. He's here. I can see him with my flashlight, and I'm going to get him."

Quig heard Tommy's feet on the rock at water's edge. He sucked in a big breath of air and began to count.

14

"I'm at nine, Tommy," he called. At the same time

he began to take off his shoes. He could feel the way better with his bare feet.

"You can't go down there, Quig," Peggy warned. "You'll break your neck."

"Ten!" counted Quig and started down.

"Don't you come down here!" screamed Tommy. "I'm getting my frog. He's sitting on the next rock. I'm getting him with my net."

Quig was over the edge now, fumbling for the first foothold. He was going down with his stomach flat against the bluff. He tightened his muscles, trying to stop the trembling in his body. There was a sudden silence from below.

"Quig, I've dropped my flashlight. It's pitch dark. I can't see! I've got my frog, but he's trying to get away."

"Don't move. I'm on the way," Quig called. His voice sounded more confident than he felt. Then he smiled to himself.

Quig heard Tommy moving on the rocks below. Suddenly he heard Tommy lurch. Then there was the sound of sliding stones and a splash into the water.

"Quig, I fell in. The current's pulling me out. I can't touch bottom."

"Grab a rock and hang on!" Quig ordered. "I'm coming."

Peggy went for help while Quig continued his climb. He had always planned to explore Dead End Bluff some day, but never like this. Now he had to do

15

it even though he was scared stiff.

"Tom, are you hanging on?"

"Uh-huh, I found a place. Hurry, Quig! Hurry! I can't hang on much longer." Tommy's voice sounded terribly frightened.

Quig couldn't hurry, he didn't dare hurry. If he fell and hurt himself, that might be all for both of them.

"You can hang on, Tommy. You've got to, just a little longer!"

Quig forced all the strength he had into his voice. He hoped he sounded strong to the little boy waiting in the darkness. That moment he felt anything but strong himself. It was one thing to think about doing this, and another to do it.

He slipped and fell a few feet, scraping his knees and his arms on the rough face of the cliff. He couldn't have far to go now. Suddenly Tommy called out, "I see you, Quig. You're down."

Quig reached with his foot and felt water. He found that he was on a flat ledge of rock. He had done it, after all these years he had done it. But strangely there was no sense of joy. He just snatched off his slacks and shirt and sat down, sliding off into the river. The current caught him and he knew what was coming. Somehow he must find Tommy in the water. He must wade as far as he could on the rocky bottom and pray that he wouldn't lose his balance.

"Here I am, Tommy," he called in as calm a voice as

17

he could manage. "Hang on. Tell me which way to go."

Now that Tommy had caught a glimmer of his brother's body through the darkness, he began to cry. With Quig actually in the river, coming toward him, all of his bravery seemed to fade away. "I—can't tell you," he sobbed. "I've got water in my nose. I can't hang on any longer. I'm going to drown!"

"You sure are if you let go now. You're going to drown if you don't keep talking to me so I know where to go. Stop that blubbering and talk to me, I tell you!"

"Come straight ahead," Tommy gulped, shocked back to control.

Quig inched his way over the rocks toward the sound of Tommy's voice. Once he slipped on a slimy stone and fell into a deep hole.

"Here I am," Tommy squeaked.

"Let's go," Quig commanded. Quig was close enough now to touch Tommy.

The place where Tommy was holding on to the rock was indeed over Tommy's head, but Quig was so much taller that he could easily stand on the bottom. The water swirled around them. Quig knew that the hardest part was still ahead of him. Coming out by himself hadn't been so bad, but returning with a heavy, frightened child would be another thing. Quig braced himself against the current, supporting Tommy. His lifesaving lessons came back to him quickly.

"Now, Tommy," Quig said urgently, "you listen to

every word I say and do exactly what I tell you."

"O.K., Quig, I will." The panic was gone from Tommy's voice now, and Quig felt sure he could count on the boy. Quig floated him on his back, squatted down in the water himself, and flung Tommy across his shoulders. In a moment they were on their way to shore. As Quig had feared, the going was very rough. The footing was so bad and the current so strong that Quig wondered if he could manage even a few yards. Without Tommy to steer him straight, it probably would have been impossible.

Far away in the village Quig heard the wail of a siren. He slid into a hole and dunked Tommy. They both came up spluttering. He heard the siren of the village squad car. He also heard the sound of the fire engine. It seemed to be coming closer. Right now all Quig wanted in the world was to set Tommy down safely at the bottom of Dead End Bluff.

A few more steps and he would have it made. Tommy had been unbelievably quiet all the way, but now he wriggled on Quig's shoulders and cried, "We're almost back!"

"Hold still," Quig ordered. "Don't upset the works now."

The wail of the sirens seemed to pierce the air above them. Then the sirens were still. Quig could hear the sound of excited voices, shouting at the top of the bluff. Above them all came Peggy's voice: "Quig! Are you all right? I've got help!"

Quig's foot struck the shore and he crawled up onto the narrow ledge. It seemed to him that half the village must have come to the rescue. He heard the voices of Officer O'Brien and Officer Barry.

"We're all right!" Quig called. "We're out of the water."

"Shine that spotlight right down the bluff, Mac," called Officer O'Brien to a fire fighter standing on top of the fire truck. "Now let's set your ladder up. We'll get those kids up here in no time."

"Nobody needs to come down here," shouted Tommy. "I fell in the river, that's all, and my brother came down to get me and he carried me out. We can come up the bluff by ourselves."

In a minute Tommy's father came to the edge of the bluff and called down.

"Quig, we've decided that we will put the ladder down and bring Tommy up. As long as the fire fighters are here, they might as well do it. It'll be a lot easier."

The long ladder was lowered carefully over the edge

of the bluff. Then Mac came down. He settled it firmly at the bottom and said, "Come on, young one, let's go up. Quig, hold it for me, just to make sure."

Mac started up the ladder carrying Tommy. Quig waited, beginning to shiver in the cool of the August evening. Mac had reached the top.

Then Quig began to search around on the ledge for his pants and shirt.

"I'm coming down for you, Quig," Mac called.

"Oh, no, you aren't," Quig called back. He would not accept help he didn't need. "If I can drag Tommy out of the rapids all alone, I guess I can climb this ladder by myself. Here I come!"

He climbed the ladder, slowly, carefully, but with perfect confidence. Quig's mother waited at the top with a firm hand to help him off.

"Well done, Quig" she said.

"Thanks, Mom," Quig responded. "Next time I'll climb the bluff without the ladder."

Focus

1. Why did Tommy go down Dead End Bluff at night?
2. Why hadn't Quig ever gone to the bottom of Dead End Bluff?
3. What part did Peggy play in the rescue?
4. How did Quig rescue Tommy?
5. Why do you think Quig refused help in getting back up the bluff?

Quig showed great courage in saving his brother from the river. Ida Lewis showed courage, too, in a different way.

IDA LEWIS

Saver of Lives

LAURENCE SWINBURNE

Huge waves crashed on the small rocky island. The wind whipped the rain against the lighthouse. Captain Hosea Lewis peered through the terrible storm. He could just barely make out the bobbing rowboat with its three passengers coming from the shore.

"Ida is coming," he told his wife. "I wish she had decided to stay on the mainland tonight."

"Don't worry," said Mrs. Lewis. "The children are safe enough." She wished her words equalled her feelings. She was as worried as her husband. But she didn't want to say so, because the captain was not a well man.

The boat would be on the tip of a wave for a moment. Then it would slide down the hill of water and be lost from view. After a moment in which the captain would hold his breath, the boat would appear again. The boat seemed to be moving ahead, but the storm was growing worse.

At last Hosea Lewis sank into a chair. He put a hand over his eyes. "I can't watch any more," he groaned. "I'm sure they will be drowned."

For the next few minutes, Mrs. Lewis stared through the windows. At last she cried, "They are almost here! Only a few more feet! They made it!"

"Thanks be to Ida," the captain said. He rose and looked down the stairs. The happy children came pounding up. Ida was the last to come.

"It's a bit of a blow out there," she said.

"We were mighty afraid, daughter," her father said.

He shook his head. "You took a big chance, and you only sixteen."

She looked at him, amazed. "I've rowed in worse, father. And what has my age got to do with it?"

Scolding words were on his lips. He held them back as she sat and pulled off her boots.

"Just look at your stockings!" exclaimed her mother. "They've become wet, and the water has turned to ice."

Ida shrugged and used scissors to cut the stockings loose from her legs. "It's nothing. My feet will be warm in a minute."

In spite of himself, the captain smiled. "In all the years I was at sea," he said, "I never saw any sailor complain less than you do, Ida. Heaven only knows how the family could get along without you."

This was praise indeed. Ida beamed. But they were true words. The girl was the center of the family. Each day she would row her younger brothers and sisters to shore so that they could attend school. She did all the shopping and brought mail and her father's medicine. They were all lucky to be so close to the mainland. People living in other lighthouses had to wait months to see the mainland.

The family had come to the small island off Newport, Rhode Island, in 1854. Ida was then twelve years old. The girl loved living in the house near the lighthouse. No weather bothered her. She enjoyed listening to the shrieking winter wind and crashing ocean as much as she liked the soft lapping of waves on a calm summer day.

Her only worry was her father. Hosea Lewis had been a captain on a government ship for many years. But he had become ill and could sail no more. Then he had been given the job of lighthouse keeper of Lime Rock. He was not well enough to handle it alone. But his family helped keep the light burning through long nights to warn ships.

It almost seemed as if Ida were born to spend her life on the island. She probably would not have been happy on the mainland. By the time she was sixteen, she was the best swimmer in Rhode Island—boy, girl, or adult.

Ida loved rowing even more than swimming. She didn't seem to mind how rough the sea was. The higher the waves, the more she liked it.

She knew how to handle a boat. But there were people in Newport who didn't. One was a boy named John King. On a fall day in 1858 he went sailing with three friends.

John liked to play jokes. He climbed up to the top of the boat's mast. When he rocked back and forth, his friends cried out in fear.

They had good reason to be frightened, for John was acting carelessly. Suddenly the boat turned over. The three boys floundered in the water, shouting.

They were lucky that Ida had been watching them. She jumped into her rowboat and rowed hard. She reached the youths just in time.

As they dried themselves off on Lime Rock, Ida said sternly, "That was a foolish trick, John. You came close to drowning."

"I know," answered the boy through chattering teeth. "But please don't tell my mother and father, Ida. They don't know I took the boat out."

Ida's heart softened. She was an agreeable girl. "I promise. But don't do it again."

That was the young woman's first sea rescue. It would not be her last. It was not until many years later that the people of Newport learned of how she had saved John King.

Throughout her long life on Lime Rock, Ida Lewis saved the lives of 23 people . . . and one sheep. It was the rescue of the sheep that tickled her funny bone. She would tell the story and then laugh with her listeners until tears ran down her cheeks.

Three men were driving a valuable sheep through Newport on a freezing winter morning. Perhaps, Ida thought, the sheep decided to run in order to keep warm. Anyway, it broke away from its handlers and dashed for the docks. The water looked inviting to the animal. It plunged into the sea.

One of Ida's brothers had rowed to the mainland to do some shopping. He had left his new boat on the beach. The sheep handlers jumped into the boat and pushed off towards the sheep.

The wind was blowing hard that day. The waves were high as house roofs. At any other time, the men might have been more careful, but now they worried more about the sheep than about their own safety. Suddenly a towering wave came down upon them. The boat overturned and the three men were tossed around in the water.

Luckily for them, Ida was watching from the Lewis house. Within a minute she was after them. Her strong arms pulled the oars with all their might. She dragged all three aboard and took them to shore.

"We'll never forget what you did for us," one of them said. He looked sadly out to sea. There his animal was being rushed along into the Atlantic Ocean by strong currents. "I only wish you had been able to get the sheep, too."

Ida shook her head and laughed. "That's bothering you, eh? Well, don't worry."

Once again Ida rowed out alone. It took her a whole hour to catch up to the frightened sheep, haul it in her boat, and return.

It was a funny story, everyone who heard it agreed. But it could have turned out far differently. It was all right for Ida to rescue people . . . but risk her life for a sheep?

"Next time let the sheep go," they begged her.

"You're worth far more than that."

And she *was* worth more! Her many rescues brought her fame. All over the country, newspapers and magazines wrote of her brave deeds. It was little wonder that, after her father died, she was named the lighthouse keeper of Lime Rock.

She received mail from all over the country. Quite a few men wrote, asking to marry her. Perhaps, she said with a smile, they wanted her as a wife because they didn't know how to swim.

She also had many visitors. Her biggest thrill came when Ulysses S. Grant, then president of the United States, stepped ashore for a chat.

On the night of October 24, 1911, Ida Lewis died at the age of 69. For 57 years, she had faithfully kept the light of Lime Rock burning.

On the night she died all the ships in Newport Harbor tolled their bells. They knew they had lost a good friend.

Focus
1. Where did Ida Lewis live?
2. The author describes Ida as the center of the family. What does this mean? Explain your answer. Give several details.
3. What were some of the things Ida could do well?
4. What rescues did the story tell about?
5. What did the story tell about Ida Lewis's fame?

In "Ida Lewis, Saver of Lives," you learned about a heroic lighthouse keeper. Just what is a lighthouse? What would it be like to live on a storm-battered island far from other people?

Lighthouses

CAROL ABARNO

Imagine that you are the captain of a ship trying to find your way into a harbor at night. You are a specialist in piloting ships, but there is nothing to light your way. Not even the moon is there to help. What would you do? If there were a storm you might lose both your ship and your crew.

Now there are lighthouses to guide sailors. What is a lighthouse? Simply stated, a lighthouse is a light set on top of some structure, such as a tower. Some lighthouses are placed at the entrance to harbors. They help sailors find their way. After all, there are no road signs or traffic officers at sea! Other lighthouses are placed on dangerous rocks as a warning. Keep Off! Stay Away! their flashing lights urge.

Kinds of Lighthouses

The first lighthouses were just bonfires on beaches or on rocks. They helped some sailors in ships offshore, but they couldn't be seen far away. Then someone got the idea of putting the fires on top of high towers. And so the idea for the lighthouse as we know it today was born.

The first of the light towers was built 2300 years ago, on an island near the country of Egypt. It was a magnificent tower, rising 400 feet into the sky. It stood for hundreds of years and led many ships safely into harbor.

Nowadays, lighthouses can be found all over the

Lantern
Room

Service
Room

Bedroom

Living
Room

Store
Room

32

world. Some are great stone towers with houses inside, where the keepers and their families live. Some are just lights standing on steel legs. No one lives in those lighthouses. Some even have been put up where there is no land, not even rocks. They stand on steel legs that have been driven deep into the ocean bottom. They do not even look like any other lighthouses. These are flat on top, and helicopters can land on them.

Still other lighthouses are really ships. They are anchored in such dangerous waters that no lighthouse could be built there.

Lighthouses in the Past

Until 1939, lighthouses were run by civilians and their families. Since then the Coast Guard has taken over all the lighthouses in the United States. Some families decided to stay in their lighthouses. They were able to share the lighthouses with the Coast Guard keepers.

Life in Lighthouses

Suppose you had lived sixty years ago, with your family, on an island lighthouse. The keeper might have been your father or your mother. What would your life have been like?

There would be no television, and likely no radio. You would be alone a lot, but hardly lonely. Your brothers and sisters would be there, and your parents.

Sea birds would always be near. All kinds of sea birds would land near your home. You would learn to feed them and they would become almost like pets.

You would likely know much more about nature than mainland children would. You couldn't help learning, because you would be living close to nature. And you would have to get used to sleeping in a new way. After all, a powerful light or a loud foghorn would be just above your bedroom!

You might not know much about common things. Snowdrifts, forests, big parties, lots of playmates, baseball games—and schoolrooms—would be unknown.

Yes, what about school? The chances of your going to a regular school would be slim. It would be too risky to get to the mainland in the winter. And once on the mainland, you might be stranded by a storm. So . . . school would come to you!

A teacher would stay with you and your family two or three weeks each year. The rest of the year your parents would teach you from books the teacher would leave.

You would go to school six days a week, from early morning until late in the evening. But you would not be bored. Everyone looked forward to the teacher's visit. And everyone hoped a storm would come then. If a storm came, the teacher could not leave to get to another lighthouse.

Lighthouse Children

Most lighthouse children made up their own games. A favorite was called "Whiz." The object was to see who could climb to the top of the highest rock first. All the players had to keep their hands behind their backs! The usual prize was two helpings of supper.

To be a lighthouse child, you would have to be strong and brave, too. Sometimes you might even have to take charge of the lighthouse. Abbie Burgess, a four-teen-year-old girl, took charge of a lighthouse many years ago. Her father, who was the keeper, and her older brother had rowed to the mainland for food. Be-cause of high seas, they could not return for 21 days. In that time Abbie had to take care of her sick mother and two younger sisters. There were two lighthouses on the island, and she had to go from one to the other to keep both lights lit. All this time a hurricane and many snowstorms roared across the island. But the lights stayed on.

The Light

When Abbie took care of those lighthouses, she lit the tower lanterns with oil. She pumped the oil from a storage tank up 100 feet to the lantern room above. Every five hours, day and night, she had to pump more oil to keep the light burning!

Lighthouse lanterns weren't always lit by burning oil. Before Abbie's time, the lanterns were lit with wood. Before wood, coal was used to light the lanterns. Hauling the wood or coal a hundred feet up a winding staircase was a lot of work.

Wood and coal were later replaced by candles. After candles, oil became the main fuel until electricity was put in. Electricity came in about 1900. Even then, electric lights were measured in "candlepower." A 100-watt bulb, for example, gives the same light as 114 candles.

To make the light much brighter the bulbs in the lanterns are put in front of cut-glass mirrors. And the lights turn, sending their beams as far as 40 miles. Each light has its own system of blinking. The light may be green, red, or white. From the colors the sailors can tell which light they are watching, even though they cannot see the tower.

Sometimes fog hides a lighthouse. Then the keeper will turn on the foghorn, which blasts a warning every few seconds. Many lighthouses have radio beams, too. Large ships can pick up the signals and know just where they are. As with the different light-blinking systems, the radio beam of each lighthouse sends its own signal.

Do you think you'd like to live on an island lighthouse? Sometimes it would be fun, and sometimes not. But nearly every boy and girl brought up in a lighthouse liked the life. In fact, many lighthouse children wanted to become keepers themselves.

"I'm going to keep a light when I grow up," was

something children often said. "I already know how it's done. I don't have to learn anymore. Besides, lighthouses help people."

Not many people can become keepers of lights anymore. More and more lighthouses are being made automatic. Computers keep the lights flashing and the foghorns booming. Only a few lights will continue to be run by people. But we will always be able to read the stories of the families that kept the lights beaming.

Focus

1. What is a lighthouse? Describe two different kinds.
2. How did lighthouse children go to school?
3. Abbie Burgess was like Ida Lewis in some ways. Tell three things that Abbie did to help when there was trouble.
4. Describe two ways that lighthouses get their lights.
5. Why are only a few lighthouses still run by people?

37

MATH READING: What's It All About?

Engineers use math to design lighthouses, and captains use math to help guide their ships.

Understanding math problems requires special reading skills. Here are some tips that will make math books easier to read.

Take a First Look

Part of a math book is printed on the next page. Take a look at the headings in large type. What do the headings tell you?

Look at the two pictures on the page. Which problem does each picture go with?

Find Key Ideas

Now look for direction words and math symbols. Note the direction word **Add** under the heading "Practice 1." The problems under that heading have the math symbol for addition (+). Now find the direction word and math symbol in the second section.

The problems in the section called "Solve These Problems" have no direction words. Read the problems and look for clue words that help you decide what to do. How do the words *combined* and *difference* help you?

Read Carefully

Check the numbers of the problems. Some pages are numbered from left to right and some from top to bottom. Also be sure that you copy the problems correctly.

Read word problems more than once. Ask yourself if you know what the problem asks, and if you have solved a similar problem before. Use the pictures as hints.

These tips on reading math books should help you to understand the pages of your math text.

ADDING AND SUBTRACTING WITH REGROUPING

Example: ADD

Step 1. add ones and regroup	**Step 2.** add tens and regroup	**Step 3.** add hundreds and regroup
1	1 1	1 1
736	736	736
+588	+588	+ 588
4	24	1324

Practice 1: ADD

1.
$$
\begin{array}{r} 496 \\ +325 \end{array}
$$

2.
$$
\begin{array}{r} 593 \\ +209 \end{array}
$$

3. $195 + 817 =$

4. $357 + 268 =$

Step 1. regroup and subtract ones	**Step 2.** regroup and subtract tens	**Step 3.** regroup and subtract hundreds
1 1	7 11 1	7 11 1
8̸2̸4	8̸ 2̸ 4	8̸ 2̸ 4
−558	−5 5 8	−5 5 8
6	6 6	2 6 6

Practice 2: SUBTRACT

5.
$$
\begin{array}{r} 223 \\ -119 \end{array}
$$

6.
$$
\begin{array}{r} 933 \\ -654 \end{array}
$$

7. $736 - 458 =$

8. $402 - 313 =$

Solve These Problems

9. A dock is 1000 feet long. One ship is 472 feet long. Another ship is 425 feet long. What is the combined length of the two ships? Can both ships dock at the same time?

10. One lighthouse is 146 feet tall. Another lighthouse is 127 feet tall. What is the difference in their heights?

CHECKPOINT

Vocabulary:
Word
Identification
Use the following words to complete the sentences below. Write the completed sentences on your paper.

elect   shrieking   dredge   confident
towering   responded   cast

1. You will catch more fish if you _____ your fishing line out from a boat than if you do it from the shore.
2. Next week the students will _____ a class president.
3. The police will _____ the river to find the sunken car.
4. I gazed in wonder at the _____ lighthouse.

Vocabulary:
Vocabulary
Development
(synonyms)
From the following word list find a synonym for each of the underlined words in the sentences below. On your paper write each sentence using the synonym in place of the underlined word.

panic   replied   shrieking   powerful
slimy   ill   lantern   jumbled

5. We used a <u>lamp</u> to help us explore the dark cave.
6. The wet seaweed felt <u>slippery</u> under my feet.
7. The speaker has a <u>strong</u>, booming voice.
8. I have been <u>sick</u> for almost a week.
9. The boys were <u>yelling</u> for help.
10. We heard the <u>terror</u> in his voice when he called up to us.
11. She was so scared she <u>confused</u> her words.
12. Ida <u>answered</u> with a nod of her head.

Read the story below. Then read the questions that follow the story. On your paper write the answers to the questions.

Comprehension: Sequence

Lighthouse children usually had very busy days. A typical day started with breakfast. Then came hauling fuel up the winding staircase to the lantern. After the morning chores the children would do their schoolwork. Playing was usually allowed after studying. Swimming and games were favorite activities during free time. In the evening, before listening to the radio, the children might help light the lantern.

13. What happened just before the children did their schoolwork?

14. What usually happened right after the children did their schoolwork?

15. What happened last?

On your paper write the word from the list that best completes each sentence below.

Decoding: Prefix ex-

| exclaim | exhausted | enchant | distract | exact |
| entitle | deliver | exit | except | explore |

16. The _____ amount of the bill was $12.50.

17. After the race Donna was completely _____.

18. "You won't be able to come in through the _____," said Frank, "because the door is locked from the outside."

19. The bear cub wandered away from its den because it wanted to _____ the woods nearby.

41

If Once You Have Slept
on an Island

If once you have slept on an island
    You'll never be quite the same;
You may look as you look the day before
    And go by the same old name,

You may bustle about in street and shop;
    You may sit at home and sew,
But you'll see blue water and wheeling gulls
    Wherever your feet may go.

You may chat with the neighbors of this and that
    And close to your fire keep,
But you'll hear ship whistle and lighthouse bell
    And tides beat through your sleep.

RACHEL FIELD

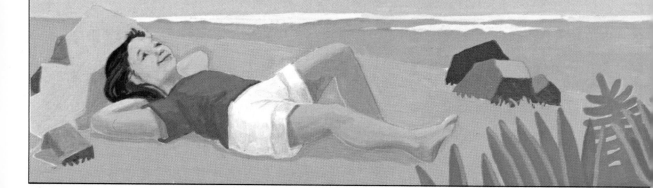

Not every island has a lighthouse warning against danger. Some islands are safe and peaceful places.

My Island Grandma KATHRYN LASKY

I have a grandmother who swims in dark sea pools. She takes me with her early in the morning. She has strong hands that hold me tight and safe in the cool water while I learn to swim.

Grandma's hands are strong. Every June she takes down the big shutters from her cabin windows. She digs the summer garden and pumps buckets full of cold water at the well. She also carries logs for the wood-burning stove.

It's very different on an island, and we live there all summer long.

In June my dad closes up his classroom, and my mom finishes painting winter things and packs her paint box full of summer colors. Then we drive away from the city. We drive all night and day until we come to the ocean where we leave our car behind and ride on a ferryboat to the island. Grandma and her dog, Shadow, are already there, waiting with a wheelbarrow to carry our suitcases to our cabin.

There is a secret path through the woods between our cabin and hers. The ground is green and soft with moss that feels like velvet blankets underneath my feet. The sunlight twinkles through the giant pine trees. It's

a greenlight world, and Grandma's cabin is on the other side by the sea. I visit her whenever I want. I just run barefoot down the green moss path to the edge of the forest where she lives.

Every day Grandma and I do wonderful summer things. In the morning, after swimming, we sit on a million-year-old rock. We wrap ourselves up in big towels and we talk about things. On our way home Grandma picks sea herbs that grow along the shore to make salad. Sometimes she gathers periwinkles, little sea snails that live on rocks, to make soup.

I hate them both.

But I love to eat the blueberries we pick in the afternoon. When we pick blueberries in the afternoon, I pretend that I am a little bear just as in the story Grandma read to me, and that Grandma is the mother bear. I growl and do bear things. I snap at her with my lips pulled over my teeth so it won't hurt. That's how baby bears get their mother's attention.

One time on our way back from picking blueberries,

Grandma called to me very softly. "Come over here, Abbey, and look at this," she said. I knew from her whispery voice that I should walk very quietly. So I tiptoed. When I got to where Grandma was standing, I saw a nest of dried grass at her feet. In the nest were three eggs—brown and gray, with little speckles all over them.

One egg was jiggling just as if there were excited little feelings all closed up inside. Then the egg bumped and rolled over, showing a big bloody gash.

"Did it hurt itself?" I asked.

"No," Grandma said, "that's the blood that comes with new life."

Inside the bloody gash I could see a small beak. It was smaller than my little fingernail. The beak was pecking its way out of the egg. Grandma said we had to go, and she pointed to the mother duck flying above. "The mother duck is angry that we're even near."

"But I want to see this baby duck get born!"

"Absolutely not, Abbey. When you're getting born you need to be left with your own kind. People with people, ducks with ducks."

Sometimes we go sailing, Grandma and Shadow and I, in a little boat called *Memory*. It's painted white with a bright green stripe. Grandma's the skipper. She steers with the tiller. I hold the ropes for the sail and pull them at important times.

When we are sailing in *Memory* and there are lots of big clouds in the sky, we tell cloud stories. Once I said, "Look, Grandma! Remember the shark Daddy told us about? There it is, swimming in the sky, chasing the baby seal. The shark won't catch the baby seal this time because there's a cloud cave, and it's just big enough for the seal pup to hide in."

Grandma says my stories are scary. She tells cloud stories about lambs and camels. Sometimes she tells about disobedient children who do not eat their vegetables. And I always say, "Please, Grandma, no vegetable stories allowed. Just tell stories about plain bad children."

We make things on rainy days. We fill a pie tin with dirt and cover the dirt with thick green moss. Then we stick in the smallest plants we can find. If you look at the moss garden for a while, it becomes a tiny world with little green mountains and trees and valleys.

Sometimes we make moon cookies and put silver

sprinkles on them.

Grandma made me a special sleeping bag for when I spend the night. On the inside the sleeping bag is dark blue with pink and lavender flowers. It's just like sleeping in a flower cave with flowers growing everywhere.

I love to shine my flashlight in the flower cave in the middle of the night. I crawl way down to the foot of the bag. It is so dark down there, I can breathe the blackness. Then I press the flashlight button and suddenly there are a million flowers jumping and hopping all over.

Sometimes when I am sound asleep, Grandma comes over to my sleeping bag. She whispers in her night voice, "Abbey, Abbey, wake up and come outside. There's something special in the sky."

I get up, and we both tiptoe out and stand barefoot in the wet grass. The night wind blows. We look up at the starry sky, and Grandma says, "Look, there's Lyra and Cygnus and Sagittarius and Capricorn." I say, "Speak English!" Grandma laughs her soft night laugh and says, "There's the Magic Harp, the Swan, the Archer, and the Sea Goat." I look up and try to find the pictures in the sky.

At the end of the summer Grandma closes up the cabin. She puts shutters on all the windows and locks the door. Then we all go back to the city.

All winter long, even though she wears shoes that

make her taller and rides subways, I know that she is really my Island Grandma who swims in dark sea pools. She makes cloud stories and star pictures and flower caves and moon cookies.

Next summer we will sail in her boat called *Memory*. She will steer, and I will pull on the ropes at important times.

Focus

1. During which season does Abbey live on an island?
2. Abbey's grandmother is a good teacher. Give two examples.
3. Of all the things that Abbey and her grandmother did, which three would you like best?
4. What happens at the end of the summer?
5. Tell a few ways that Abbey's island is different from Ida Lewis's island.

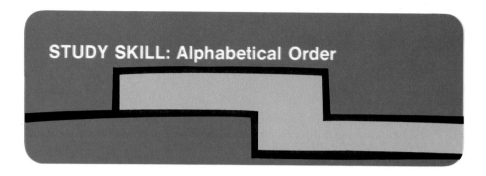

You may have heard the saying, "It's as easy as ABC." We all know the ABC's, so we can use them to organize information. Information organized by the ABC's is easier to find. Topics in reference books, such as dictionaries and encyclopedias, are arranged alphabetically. *Class* comes before *corn,* for example, and *party* comes before *potato.* Does *hockey* come before *household*?

Below is a list of entries from part of an index of a book that Abbey might have used in school.

Shoes, 58–64
    how they are made
      and used, 58
    sale of, 64
    types, 59
Snow, 139, 152
Soap, 128, 129
Soaring, 22
Soccer, 29–32
    countries in which it
      is played, 32

    field, 29
    players, 30
Sociology, 141–144
    application, 142–144
    study of, 141
Socrates, 119
Sound Waves, 28
Sourdough, 59
South America, 198
Spaghetti, 16

An index is usually at the back of a book. It lists all the topics that are in a book and tells you the pages on which those topics can be found.

50

Find the topic **Sourdough** in the index. Notice that it is listed after the topic **Sound Waves.** The first three letters in the words *sour* and *sound* are the same. How do you know which will be listed first? Look to the fourth letter. Since *n* comes before *r* in the alphabet, **Sound Waves** is listed before **Sourdough.** Sometimes you

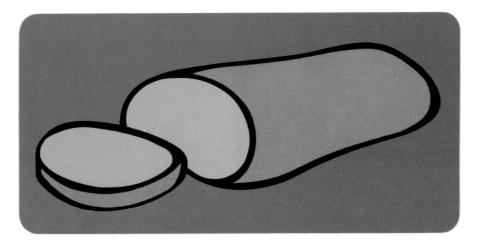

have to look to the fourth letter in words before you can alphabetize them correctly.

After you have studied the sample index, answer the following questions.

1. Give some other examples of information that is organized alphabetically.
2. How would you use an index if you were looking for specific facts to include in a report?
3. How can you tell whether the topic **Sound Waves** will be found before or after the topic **Sourdough** in an index?
4. Suppose you wanted information on Spain. How can you tell whether information on that topic is in a particular book? Describe the steps you would follow.
5. Look at the Table of Contents of your reading book. Why isn't a table of contents as helpful as an index for finding specific information?

Abbey and her grandmother shared experiences and feelings. See how Christopher, in "The Foundling," expresses his feelings and shares his experiences.

THE FOUNDLING

CAROL CARRICK

The Tilton family next door to Christopher had a new dog. It was still a puppy, really. He had come through the gate one day when Christopher got home from school.

Christopher sat down next to the puppy and scratched his head. The puppy had rings around his eyes and his dark ears. He looked the way Christopher's dog, Bodger, must have looked when Bodger was a puppy. Christopher didn't remember because he had been a baby then himself.

The puppy sniffed at Christopher's lunch box, trying to nuzzle it open. Christopher fed him the scrap of uneaten sandwich inside. After that, the puppy waited for him every day after school.

Bodger had been killed in an accident with a pickup truck. Still, Christopher found himself hoping every night that his bedroom door would be shoved open and

Bodger's warm weight would settle on his feet. The bad dreams that came for weeks after the accident had stopped. Christopher didn't lie awake any more, reliving the accident. But it was hard getting used to Bodger being gone.

Maybe it was seeing Christopher play all week with the little dog from next door that gave his father the idea. On Saturday his father came out and nodded toward the car. Christopher was bouncing a ball off the roof of the car.

"Hop in. I've got a surprise for you."

Christopher felt excited and wondered what the surprise could be. They stopped in front of a small building with a sign out front that said "ANIMAL SHELTER." Christopher's head snapped toward his father in panic.

"We're going to get a dog," Christopher said. "Dad, I don't want another one."

His father put a hand on Christopher's shoulder. "Just come in with me. It can't hurt to look. Can it?"

"Please, Dad. There won't ever be another dog like Bodger."

"I know," his father said very quietly.

For the first time Christopher realized that his father missed Bodger, too.

After ringing a bell, they went inside to a waiting room. A woman in a white coat came through an inner door.

"This is Christopher," his father said. "Christopher, I want you to meet Dr. Flores."

"I hear you like dogs, Chris," the doctor said with a friendly smile.

Christopher knew his father would be angry with him if he were rude, so he gave the woman a half smile. Then he put his hands in his pockets and stared again at the floor.

The doctor led them to a long white room with a cement floor and tile walls. At either end, dogs were in cells like a jail. There was a table and sink to one side. Everything was very clean.

"Why aren't they making any noise?" Christopher asked.

"Most of these animals are sick," the doctor explained. "They get plenty noisy when they're ready to go home. Here's the fellow who would like to meet you."

When they stopped in front of a row of small cages, a spotted puppy stood up on his hind legs. He shoved his gumdrop nose between the bars and wagged his tail furiously.

"Boy, he's a lively one," Christopher's father laughed. "He really wants to get out of there."

"Mmm," answered Christopher without much enthusiasm.

The doctor opened the cage door and lifted out the puppy. "Here. Would you like to hold him?" she

55

asked.

Christopher only shrugged in reply, but he took the puppy anyway.

"After vacation time we get a lot of cats and dogs that people abandon when they go back to the city," the doctor said. "If they weren't brought here, most of these animals would get sick or starve."

Christopher held the puppy to his face. It felt silky and warm. He could hear how fast its heart was beating.

"How about it, Christopher. Would you like to keep him?" his father asked.

A big dog lying with its leg in a cast raised its head and thumped its tail. From another cage, a sheep dog with patches of hair shaved off was watching. It seemed as if the whole room were waiting for him to answer.

Christopher shook his head. "I don't really want to," he said slowly. "I'm sorry."

When Christopher got into the car he wasn't so sure that he had made the right decision. The trip home seemed to take forever. Neither he nor his father said anything. Christopher knew he ought to explain why he didn't want the puppy except he didn't exactly know himself. He only knew how he felt. But he did feel guilty about the puppy in the cage.

"Dad, if we don't take the puppy, do you think someone else will?"

"They might."

"Don't you think it would be unfaithful to Bodger to get another dog . . . right away, I mean?"

"Christopher, it might be a good way to show that you loved having Bodger—if you rescued another little dog and took care of him."

"Well, I don't want another dog. At least not that dog. I don't want just any dog."

As the car pulled up in the driveway, Christopher's mother came out of the house. "Where's the puppy?" she asked. "I can't wait to see him."

She looked at Christopher's face, then at his father's. "What's the matter? What's happened?"

Christopher picked up his bike from where it had been left on the lawn.

"I don't want another dog," he said. "Do I have to take one just because no one else wants it? Why don't you let me alone?" And he pedaled off.

After he had gotten away from the house, Christopher cruised around, thinking. Would he have chosen Bodger the first time he saw him? he wondered. Bodger had always just been there, like his parents. He loved them without thinking about it. Now they were only trying to help him, and he'd let them down. Maybe he should go home and tell them he would take the puppy after all.

He stopped at the town dock to watch as a crowd gathered to board the ferry. Christopher recognized the puppy from next door. He was running up to people, wagging his tail hopefully and getting tangled in their feet.

After the ferry left the slip, the puppy joined some kids who were fishing. He sniffed a landed snapper and then jumped back when the fish flapped on the dock. The boys laughed as the puppy regained enough courage to bark at the fish. But when he knocked over their bait pail, they chased him off.

Christopher picked up the puppy.

"You're pretty far from home. You'd better come back with me."

He wrapped the puppy in his jacket and stuffed him in his bicycle basket. On the way back the puppy wriggled free enough to poke out his head. His ears had flopped inside out.

"You really are cute," Christopher said. "You look like my old panda bear. His name was Ben."

When they got home Christopher brought the puppy to the back of the house next door.

"Here's your dog, Mrs. Tilton. I found him on the dock. He was lost." Christopher felt quite proud of himself.

"My dog? That's not my dog," said Mrs. Tilton. "No sir! I wouldn't even let it in the house. My husband says, 'Give the poor thing something to eat. It's starving.' Oh no. You give these stray animals food and that's it. You can't get rid of them for anything."

Christopher scooped up the puppy, who had been

pulling the laces from his shoe. A wonderful idea swelled inside him until a grin spread across his face. As he left Mrs. Tilton's yard her voice continued from somewhere between the sheets she was taking down.

"It's these summer people. They can't resist getting a cute little puppy. Then, when it comes time to go home, they just dump it and expect other people to take care of it. Well, not me. . . ."

Her voice was cut off as the back door banged shut behind Christopher. His parents had already started lunch.

"Say, Mom," Christopher said, "do we have something I can give Ben to eat? He's really starved."

"You shouldn't feed the Tiltons' dog," she said. "He already has a home."

"No, Mom. That's just it. He doesn't belong to anyone."

Christopher opened the refrigerator door. With Ben wriggling under one arm, he rummaged through the shelves looking for something a puppy might eat— *his* puppy.

Focus

1. What had happened to Christopher's dog Bodger?
2. Why didn't Christopher want to get a new dog?
3. How did his father try to help him feel better?
4. How did Christopher feel when he left the shelter?
5. What happened at the end of the story?

61

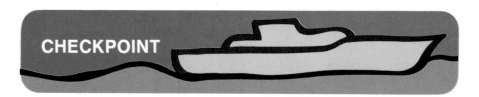

CHECKPOINT

On your paper write the six vocabulary words listed below. Next to each one write the word or phrase that means about the same as the vocabulary word.

1. skipper   a kind of metal

2. hind   protective covering for a window

3. enthusiasm   desert or withdraw from

4. lavender   pale purple color

5. abandon   rear

6. shutter   captain of a boat

                             excitement

                             to explore

Answer each question below by replacing the underlined word with an antonym from the list.

Example: Is it noisy in a library?

            No, it is quiet in a library.

narrow   awake   tight

rough   quietly   brave

7. Do you talk <u>loudly</u> when everyone is sleeping?

8. Is a <u>skinny</u> hallway wide?

9. Is a sky diver <u>cowardly</u>?

10. Are you usually <u>asleep</u> in the afternoon?

11. When there are big waves is the water <u>smooth</u>?

12. Is the knot too <u>loose</u>?

Abbey, Grandma, and Christopher are the main characters in the stories you have just read. They all have special feelings and special character traits. Choose the word in each sentence below that best fits each character. Write the completed sentence on your paper.

Comprehension: Character

13. Abbey (admires, dislikes, bores) her grandmother.

14. Grandma is a (wise, unhappy, bossy) person.

15. Christopher feels (frightened, sad, worried) about Bodger.

16. Christopher's parents are (kind, thoughtless, mean).

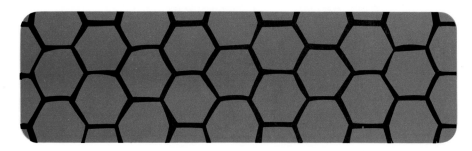

Lists of words or subjects are often organized alphabetically. Below are four lists of words. On your paper, write each list in alphabetical order.

Study Skill: Alphabetical Order

17. tiller, tile, tilt, tiling

18. deceive, decay, declare, decision

19. recognize, receive, recall, recite

20. congress, confront, connect, conduct

Christopher learned that making people happy is one way to be generous. Clowns spend their lives trying to make people happy. How do people learn to be clowns?

Clown College

CHARLENE L. KNAPP

How would you like to go to a school where you learned to ride elephants? In this school you could also learn to juggle things, and you could watch movies of famous clowns. School would last only eight weeks, and what is more, the tests would be the best part. All you would have to do is make people laugh!

Before you decide that's the school for you, you should know something else. The school is not as easy as you think. It might not be as much fun as you think, either. Thousands of people ask to go every year, but fewer than fifty students are let in. The students work from 8:30 in the morning till 10:00 at night. The school is called Clown College.

Clown College began in 1968 in Venice, Florida. It was opened by the Ringling Brothers and Barnum & Bailey Circus. The college was started because most of the circus clowns were getting old. They were about to retire and there were no younger clowns to take their places. Something had to be done. After all, what would a circus be without clowns?

All the teachers at Clown College are professional clowns. In fact, they are the best. They have to be, because it is hard to teach other people how to be clowns.

Every act involves one or more of six tricks. In one, the clown will fall down. In another, the clown will hit someone or something. In still others, the clown will mimic, or copy, a person or thing. The clown will act foolish, or do tricks, or surprise people.

Each of these six tricks may seem simple, but they are not at all simple. The clown must make them look simple. That is why clowns spend hour after hour practicing each trick.

To a clown, timing is very important. Clown College teaches students that how a trick is done is as important as why it is done. You may have seen the trick in which one clown is about to sit down. Suddenly, another clown pulls the chair away, and . . . thud! The first clown ends up on the floor, with everyone else laughing. The trick may look easy, but if the chair is pulled away too soon, the trick is ruined. Or if people think the first clown knows what is going to happen, no one will laugh. To be funny, the trick has to be a surprise. Surprise comes from timing. The clown must know exactly when to do the right—or wrong!—thing.

Of course there is more to clowning than pulling chairs from beneath people. Clowns have to be good acrobats, too. The clown who missed the chair has to know how to fall without being hurt.

Many clowns are excellent horse riders, too. Have you ever seen the trick in which a clown runs into the ring along with the bareback riders? Dressed like an ordinary person, the clown begs to be allowed to ride one of the horses. Finally, the clown is allowed to ride. Then the clown leaps for the horse, only to miss. The horse continues to trot around the ring. The clown gets up, chases the horse, and finally struggles onto the horse's back. Then the clown almost falls a second time. By now the audience is getting nervous. Who is this person? Will the person be hurt? At that moment, the rider stands upright on the horse's back, then does a perfect somersault. Now the audience knows! This is a clown. The clown has been teasing the audience! This trick is based on timing and surprise.

Learning to ride a horse like that is only one skill taught at Clown College. Tumbling, walking a high wire, and running on stilts are others. Clowns also

learn how to mime. That means to act something out without talking. Student clowns learn how to mime a wind-up toy or a bouncing ball, for example.

Whatever the trick, the student clown has to learn how to exaggerate the movements. Why is that? Circuses are held in huge arenas. Many people sit high up, far away from the action. Clowns have to make sure that everyone knows what is going on. Since clowns seldom talk, the way to be sure everyone knows what is going on is to exaggerate every movement.

Try exaggerating a movement yourself. Suppose you want to show that you are understanding an idea. First, press one finger to your forehead, to show that you are thinking. Then raise your eyebrows as high as you can. At the same time, open your mouth wide— but do it slowly. Practice in front of a mirror to see if you can convince yourself. Then try it in front of your friends.

Many clowns do the same tricks. But no two clowns will wear the same face. In fact, no clown would think of copying the face of another clown. That is why making up the face is a very important subject at Clown College. Clowns don't just paint on any funny face. First they decide what kinds of people they are. Then they paint faces to bring out their personalities. Putting on makeup is an art, so students at Clown College must learn to be artists.

Some clowns have sad faces, with shining teardrops

glued beneath their eyes. Others may look like hoboes, with tattered clothes, black paint for beards, and huge red bulbs for noses.

Just as no two clowns look alike, every clown in real life is a different kind of person. Some were college students once. Others were engineers or farmers or cheerleaders. Some are men, some are women. There are giant clowns and clowns who are little people.

Of course, not every student who graduates from Clown College is hired by a circus. Nor does every graduate want to be a circus clown. Some clowns like to work cheering up people in hospitals or performing in shopping malls.

But every student at the Clown College wants to be a clown more than anything else. One graduate of Clown College sums it up this way: "Why did I come here? Why do I want to be a clown? That's easy. I wanted to become a clown because clowns can do anything!"

Focus

1. How is Clown College different from other schools?
2. Why was Clown College started?
3. Why do clowns have to learn to exaggerate?
4. What is unusual or special about each clown's face? Give some examples.
5. Not all graduates of Clown College get jobs in circuses. Where else do clowns work?

69

LIFE SKILL: Advertisements

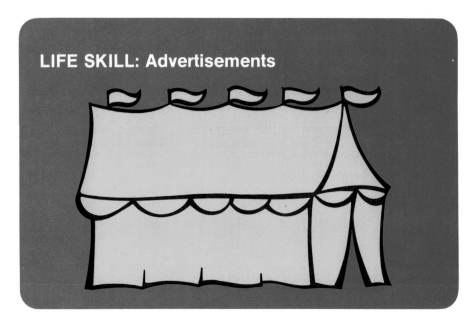

When the circus comes to town, people see circus posters everywhere. These posters provide information about the circus. Look at the circus poster.

This poster is an advertisement. It has a picture that makes you want to see the circus. It also gives the facts that will help you plan your trip to the circus.

The poster tells you such things as dates, times, prices, and locations. It also gives general information about the circus.

Look at the circus poster to answer the following questions. Write your answers on a sheet of paper.

1. Why do you think a circus uses advertisements?
2. Tell a day and a time that you could see the circus in Venice, Florida.
3. How many shows does the circus offer each day?
4. Where can you buy tickets?
5. How long do you think each show lasts? How can you tell?
6. What acts might you see at the circus?
7. What else does the poster tell you about the circus?

THE
RAWLINGS
FAMILY
CIRCUS

DAILY SHOWS
1:00 P.M.
4:00 P.M.
7:00 P.M.

TRAPEZE
ARTISTS

TIGHTROPE
WALKERS

WILD ANIMAL
TRAINERS

DANCING
BEARS

BARE BACK
RIDERS

LINCOLN ARENA
100 LINCOLN AVENUE
VENICE, FLORIDA

TICKETS ARE
AVAILABLE AT
THE CIRCUS
AND PERFORMANCE
TICKET OFFICES

CLOWNS

Sometimes making people happy can be a serious thing. Pepe the clown found that out on a ship far out at sea.

THE STORY OF
PEPE
THE CLOWN
JAMES KRÜSS

On a windy October day, a Spanish circus was aboard a ship. The circus was sailing toward the Canary Islands, where it was to give a performance. All the

circus people were in a good mood except Pepe, the clown. For the four days since they had left Barcelona, Pepe had not been feeling well. No one, except the other circus people, suspected that this old man was a clown.

There was a steady west wind to keep the boat sailing smoothly. Pepe's illness couldn't have come from rough waters. Pepe kept to himself. For four days the corners of his mouth pointed downward.

On the fifth day of the trip the wind changed. The sky darkened from minute to minute and the waves became higher and higher. Soon everyone knew that a storm was approaching. Rain was in the air, and the ship began to sway. It was lifted up high and then fell swiftly into the valley of the waves. Suddenly, with a crash of a wave, the ship lost its rudder.

The clown Pepe, who could not stand to be inside,

hung to the wooden railing of the deck. He was soaked from head to toe. Then he heard the mate holler through the megaphone. "Captain, the steering wheel no longer works." The words were so frightening that Pepe broke into an ice-cold sweat. The captain shouted at Pepe, "Go down into the cabin, sir. I can't have anyone fall overboard!" The captain guided the old clown to the room on the bridge where the mate stood. The mate was trying to steer the ship.

Pepe, still in shock, felt the warmth of the room. He heard a door slam as he fell with a plop into a chair.

The captain and the mate took no notice of him. But Pepe noticed the two men. He saw the captain step to the steering wheel to turn it around with his strong hands. He saw the mate move back with an eerie expression.

"The steering mechanism must have been

shattered!" the mate shouted to the captain.

Heavily and slowly the captain nodded. He said just loud enough for Pepe to hear, "There's nothing we can do, Mate, absolutely nothing!"

The mate then replied very softly. Pepe heard "Passengers . . . panic . . . keep quiet."

All of a sudden, the corners of the clown's mouth pointed up. He straightened up, and told the two officers, "I will give a performance."

"What kind of performance?" the captain shouted back over the breaking waves.

"I am a clown, captain! Within ten minutes I will be in my costume." The captain and the mate looked at one another as Pepe hurried out.

"Is he serious, Captain?"

"What did you say? Speak a little louder!"

"I said, is he serious? Does he think he can keep the

passengers from panicking by performing a circus act?"

"We have a rudderless ship in a hurricane," said the captain. "So we must give the clown a chance. Maybe he can distract the passengers."

"That's madness, Captain!" the mate yelled.

"No," the captain calmly replied. "At the moment there is no panic, Mate. If the clown can't help us, then we'll have to think of something else. But not until then. See to it that the passengers are brought to the salon! All of them! And keep the engines running as if the ship were on course!"

The crew carried out the captain's orders. Those passengers who were really seasick were allowed to stay in bed.

The passengers who were well came to the salon. Lamps were lit and the chairs were fastened to the floor. Then the captain appeared and told them in a

loud voice that everything on the ship was in good order. They simply had to wait for the storm to wear itself out. Therefore it had been decided to entertain the passengers with a performance.

The captain was going to give a more complete explanation, but suddenly the salon door behind him jumped open. Something colorful rolled in behind his feet. It was Pepe, the clown, with his made-up face, his baggy pants, and his much too large white gloves.

Pepe came in so quickly that everyone started laughing. They laughed even harder as Pepe tried to tickle the captain with a long outstretched finger. Then Pepe did a somersault. Getting up, he slid back and forth, tipping and rolling and even holding onto passengers for support. It all seemed very funny.

Finally Pepe straightened up and put his hand into the captain's coat pocket. The captain bent down and

whispered into Pepe's ear, "Keep it up. Hold their attention long enough for me to organize the ship and crew for a rescue. Please help us!"

Pepe whispered, "I am trying to do my best!"

Then Pepe fell back to the floor and tried in vain to do a headstand. The audience howled with laughter. The captain left to direct the crew.

For two hours Pepe entertained the people. His performance was the best he had ever given. It was a challenge for him to perform for the other circus people as well as the regular passengers. He did somersaults, he tumbled, he did strange dances, and he told funny stories. One by one, the passengers began shouting out loud.

"Under the tent it was never as splendid as it is here!" cried Ramon, the trapeze artist.

Next, Pepe performed on a violin that was only as

long as two fingers. It seemed to him a perfect grand finale. Just as he finished, the captain came back to the salon. He was pleased and astonished to see the passengers in such high spirits.

Once more Pepe threw his arms around the captain. A great cry of laughter arose from the audience. Then the captain said softly, "We have water in the ship. My people are working at the pumps. I do not know how long we can hold out. How long can you carry on?"

The bad news affected the exhausted Pepe more than the captain had expected. The corners of Pepe's mouth turned down. "I don't know how long I can go on, Captain."

The old clown did not give up. He ran through his whole show again, finding one soothing piece after another to play on his violin. Finally he had to grasp the back of a chair to steady his right leg. He was so tired

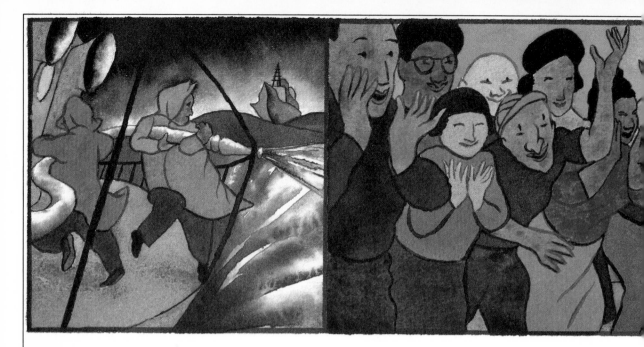

that he nearly fell down.

For almost an hour more, Pepe entertained everyone with his violin.

During this hour, half the crew labored at the pumps. Nearby, a rescue boat waited. As soon as the waters were still enough, it would move in to help the ship and its passengers.

Pepe was just starting his final number when the captain reappeared in the salon. The captain wanted to give everybody a message, but he stopped. He didn't want to interrupt the beautiful music Pepe was playing on his violin.

Pepe concluded his concert with a deep bow. The people applauded and shouted "Encore!" But the captain bowed to the clown and whispered into his ear, "The rescue ship is here!"

The corners of Pepe's mouth went up and spread

almost to his ears. Then his arms began to dangle, and the tiny violin and the tiny bow fell as Pepe fainted against the captain. The large red mouth with the white face was still grinning.

Focus

1. Where does this story take place?
2. What happened to the ship?
3. Why did Pepe offer to perform?
4. Tell a few ways that Pepe entertained his audience.
5. What happened to Pepe when the captain whispered in his ear that the rescue ship had arrived?

Pepe the clown performed for audiences. Marsha also wanted to perform for audiences—until she saw Uncle Richard's skates.

The Skates of Uncle Richard

CAROL FENNER

Once there was an ice-skating champion, a beautiful figure skater. She was tall and slender. She could swoop across the ice and leap into a double turn high in the middle of the air. She could spin so fast she could hardly be seen except for a whirling blur.

Her hair was braided into tight little ropes across her head. She had brown eyes that shone in a round face. Her picture was in the paper on the sports page. Television cameras followed her around while she skated so that people could watch her in their living rooms.

But there was only one person who knew where she lived. A girl named Marsha knew—because the beautiful figure skater lived inside Marsha's dreams. Marsha also dreamed of being a figure skater herself, tall and slender and able to spin and fly across the ice.

In the audience of her dream sat her mother and father. Her father's face was smiling and he would clap his big hands gently to the music. Her older brother Leonard was always there, too. They all watched as she skated in the silvery arena. She never missed a turn. She never moved out of step with the music. She never fell down.

In her wide-awake, real life, Marsha had been watching the championship skaters on television ever since she was six. A part of Marsha always skated with the skaters she watched, seemed to breathe when they breathed.

Marsha had never seen a black skater on TV until the year she turned eight. Then, suddenly, there she was, whipping across the screen, a bold figure against the ice. Marsha's mouth dropped. The skater never faltered; she finished her piece with a slow, melting spin. Marsha let her breath out with the spin. Her dream was beating fiercely in her heart.

Marsha had never skated with real ice skates on real ice. But sometimes she skated without skates. Alone in her room, her arm lifted, she would bend forward and extend one leg behind.

Her older brother Leonard had ice skates with long, straight racing blades. He had mowed lawns one summer and bought them with the money he earned. Marsha's birthday was coming. She hinted to her mother that she would like ice skates for her birthday present.

"Maybe," was all her mother would say.

Finally her birthday came. Marsha's parents gave her a large box covered with red tissue. It had silver stars pasted into the shape of her initial, a big starry "M." Her heart crowded into her throat.

When she opened it up, there inside the whispering tissue were the ugliest ice skates she had ever seen.

For a while, Marsha just sat staring at the skates. Then dumbly she took them out of the box. They were old-fashioned hockey skates, with brown leather around the thick toes and brown circles at the ankles. They had heavy, blunted blades meant for stopping short and turning hard. They were not in the least the kind of skates she had in mind.

"They were your Uncle Richard's," said her mother. "They were his skates when he was seven. He was about your size then. He kept them in good condition. They're almost good as new."

Marsha kept her eyes on the skates. Uncle Richard was old now . . . at least thirty. She could feel tears pushing to get out from behind her eyes.

"Your Uncle Richard is a fine skater," her mother continued. "He learned how to skate on those skates. They'll be a good start for you, Marsha, till we see how you take to skating."

Marsha sat on the floor with the box at her side, the skates in her lap. "I remembered packing them away in the attic years ago," her mother was saying. "Richard'll be pleased to know they're being used."

But Marsha was feeling the beautiful black champion of her dreams disappear. The music and the arena were fading away. There in her lap lay the ugliest skates in the world.

One Saturday morning, several weeks after her birthday, Marsha went to her closet and took out the hockey skates. She sat on her bed and tried them on. They were actually a pretty good fit. She stood up on them. They wobbled. Her ankles wobbled. She clutched the edge of the bed. "It's because there's no ice," she thought. "It'll be all right if there's ice."

At lunchtime she asked Leonard if he would take her to the rink with him. "Of course," Leonard said.

After lunch Marsha and Leonard walked the mile to the skating rink. They sat on the cold bench to put on their skates. Leonard laced up rapidly. Then he stood up impatiently. He waved to some friends skating out on the ice. "Hurry up, will you?" he said to Marsha.

Marsha laced her skates and stood up. Her feet felt like blocks of wood. "Come on, Marsha," Leonard said. She took a step onto the ice. Suddenly the skates slipped away as if they were trying to escape from her feet. Up into the air went her legs. Down onto the ice went Marsha.

Leonard laughed as he helped her up.

Whooooooooosh! Up into the air went Uncle Richard's skates. Down onto the ice again went Marsha. "Hey, there, watch yourself," laughed Leonard again. He hauled her up by one arm. But her legs kept going in different directions.

Leonard grabbed both of her hands. "Now," he ordered, "keep hold of my hands and keep your ankles straight." Then he began to skate backward, pulling Marsha forward. Her ankles caved in; her ankles bent out. Back and forth, in and out. She wobbled forward on Uncle Richard's skates.

It was no fun. Marsha kept falling down. Her ankles began to ache. Finally Leonard took her to a bench and left her there. "You'd better rest awhile," he said, and skated off to his friends.

Marsha sat on the bench alone. Her fingers were numb with cold. Tears tickled behind her nose and clogged her head. She wanted to go home, but she would have to wait for Leonard.

Suddenly a man was standing in front of her. He

was smiling. She was so wrapped up in unhappiness that at first she didn't know him. He was very tall. A long, red scarf trailed over one shoulder. She saw that he was leaning toward her, saying something, and she saw his beautiful black cloud of hair. Then she recognized her Uncle Richard.

He was saying, "Marsha girl, is that you? Why are you looking so sad?" Marsha didn't know what to say.

"They were your first skates when you were seven," she explained in a low voice. Uncle Richard knelt down in front of her and took one of her feet in both of his hands. He whispered, "They sure are . . . they sure are. . . ." He looked up at her with delight growing in his face. "Those good old skates." He laughed. Then he began to undo the laces and Marsha thought he was going to take the skates back. But he was saying, "First off, Marsha, you've got to have your skates laced properly. Your feet are falling out of these. They're laced up all wrong."

Uncle Richard straightened the tongue in her boot. He left the bottom lacings loose so she could wiggle her toes. Then he laced very tightly and evenly across her foot and above her ankle.

Uncle Richard stood her up and began to pull her slowly and evenly across the ice. "Bend your knees, not your middle," he told her. Marsha bent her knees and her middle straightened right up. She was surprised at how easily she could balance now.

After they had gone a short distance, Uncle Richard said, "You do that easily, so I want to show you some things to practice here while I get some skating done. Watch closely."

He pushed forward onto one foot and trailed the other behind lightly without touching the ice. "Just bend your knee and lean into it," he said, "nice and easy."

Then he brought the other foot forward and pushed easily onto that one. "I push," he said, "and then I glide . . . and then I push with the other foot. And then I glide!" Uncle Richard glided forward, first on one foot and then the other. "Push, glide . . . push, glide. Get it?" Marsha nodded.

"Now you practice that for a while. Okay?" Marsha nodded again and Uncle Richard skated off, his red scarf trailing.

Uncle Richard moved slowly across the ice. Then Marsha saw him reach into his pocket and pull out a tiny radio. He held it next to his ear and began to skate to music no one else could hear. Marsha noticed how he glided a long time on one foot before he shifted his weight to the other one. Then he made some smooth, neat turns. His speed quickened as he circled into a spin. The red scarf whipped around him and gradually began to unwind.

"Oh," breathed Marsha. "Oh, he is fine. He is really fine."

People began to stop skating and watch Uncle Richard, who now turned and sped forward. Suddenly he swooped and leapt into a single axel, fine as any Olympic skater. He circled to a halt and began to skate backward again.

Alone in the middle of the ice, Marsha said to

herself, "Well, I can't stand here forever." She tested herself, lifting first one foot and then the other. She took a few timid steps. She skidded a little. She glided a little. She stopped and rested.

Then she took a deep breath, bent her knee, and pushed off onto her right foot the way Uncle Richard had done. It worked! Push, glide . . . push, glide.

She gasped with excitement. It was fun! She tried it again. She pushed off more boldly and glided farther. She did it over again. And again.

Suddenly she realized she was at the other end of the rink. "My, my," said a voice behind her. "I thought I left you down at the other end." It was Uncle Richard. He was turning off his radio and smiling. "How'd you get here?" he asked.

"I push-push-glided," said Marsha. "All by myself. No one helped."

"You are one surprising young lady," said Uncle Richard. "You learn fast."

Marsha felt, in that moment, that Uncle Richard could see inside her heart better than anyone. The beautiful figure skater of her dreams floated briefly into her mind, but Marsha didn't have time for her now.

"I want to learn how to skate the way you skate," she said. Uncle Richard touched her cheek softly with his fingertips. He looked very thoughtful for a minute. Then he said quietly, "Okay. We'll work on it."

Uncle Richard stood up. "First off, don't leave your

body all bundled down inside your coat. Don't watch your feet. Stretch up. Be proud, but not stiff. Look where you're going. Reach for the sky . . . or the moon . . . or a tree top.

"You're a natural," said Uncle Richard. "You can be a super fine skater. But you'll have to set your mind to it."

"Okay," she said, feeling very warm and sure.

"Now you keep practicing," said Uncle Richard. "Next week we'll have another lesson." Marsha beamed at him. He added, "They're a good old pair of skates. Oil the runners, you hear?"

Uncle Richard pushed off. She watched him glide away. Other people watched him, too. He turned up the radio again and held it to his ear.

Marsha pushed off after him. Push, glide . . . push, glide. Past her staring brother she skated. Hardly even a wobble. Proud, not stiff. She glided away on the skates of Uncle Richard, taller and taller, never once falling down.

Focus

1. What was Marsha's dream?
2. Why was Marsha's birthday disappointing?
3. What was Marsha's first experience on the ice like?
4. How did Uncle Richard help Marsha?
5. At the end of the story, what did Marsha and Uncle Richard plan to do?

CHECKPOINT

Read the paragraph below and choose the word from the list that best completes each sentence. Write the completed paragraph on your paper.

personalities   impatiently   exhausted
falter   timid   initial   properly

Some people believe that many clowns have similar (1) . Clowns are usually very outgoing people. They are rarely (2) . Clowns need to think and act quickly. For instance, if they should (3) while attempting a trick, they must recover and pretend that the mistake was part of the act! Studying to be a clown is hard work. It takes time to learn to make people laugh. People learning to be clowns should not do their work (4) . They should also expect to be (5) at the end of the day.

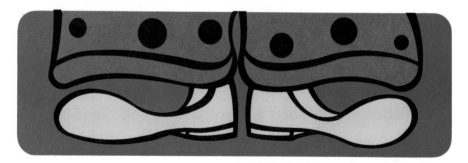

The things people do or say tell you about their characters. Think about the people in the stories you have just read. Then read each of the following questions. Choose the word that best answers each question. Write each word on your paper.

6. Which word best describes people who graduate from Clown College?

    hard-working   lazy   dull

7. Which word best describes Pepe's actions during the emergency?

    useless   silly   brave

8. Which word tells something about Uncle Richard?

    helpful   afraid   sad

9. Marsha wanted new ice skates. Which word best describes Marsha's feelings when she opened her birthday present?

    grateful   disappointed   generous

10. Which word best describes Marsha's feelings when she learned to skate?

    selfish   frightened   proud

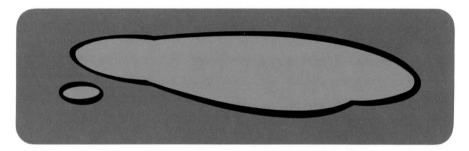

Decide which of the following words best completes each sentence. Write the completed sentences on your paper.

Decoding: Suffixes *-ist, -ible, -able*

    adjustable   undigested   curing   correctable
    correction   nonadjustable   curable   digestible

11. Because my answer was written in ink, my mistake was not _____.

12. Infants eat baby food because it is more _____ than solid food.

13. The doctor was happy to tell her patient that his condition was _____.

14. Bicycle seats can be moved up or down to fit the rider. The seats are _____.

A Rustle of

Surroundings are the things around people. Buildings, people, weather, plants, and even the sound of rustling leaves are part of the surroundings.

Surroundings affect people in many ways. The stories that follow show some of those ways. In one story a young camper explores his surroundings.

Other stories involve animals and people. One animal finds itself caught in surroundings that people have changed.

In all the stories people are affected by their surroundings. Whatever happens, though, the people learn about life. Try to discover how.

aves

Your Own Best Secret Place

His name is
William Cottonwood.

That's all
I know about him . . .
just that
and
the way
he loved
a secret place
he had to
leave.

I think of
William Cottonwood
a lot.

I wish I knew
where
he is
now.

I'd tell him
how
I found
his secret place
and how
I'm
taking care of it
and that
I hope
he doesn't mind
my being there.

Or
you
could tell him
for me.

If you ever meet
somebody
and his name is
William Cottonwood
and he used to live
by the Rio Grande River
in a valley
in New Mexico where
there are
chile farms
and cornfields . . .
then
ask him
if
he left

three messages
nailed up
on a hollow tree.

If he says
yes,
then he's
the William Cottonwood
I'm looking for.

Tell him
this
for me.

Just say
I found his place
by accident.

BYRD BAYLOR

Sometimes familiar surroundings can seem strange. Seth found that out when his friend Daniel dared him to stay overnight in the woods . . . alone.

Last Days of Brightness, Part 1

Adapted from SNOWSHOE TREK TO OTTER RIVER by DAVID BUDBILL

October. It was one of those perfect October days, crisp and cool as a carrot. The sky was a cloudless, turquoise blue.

It wouldn't be long now before the days of color and light gave way to cold November rain. But not yet. These were the last days of brightness, and Seth meant to use them well. He had gotten up before the sun, had a light breakfast, and packed his gear. He had gone down to the barn, where his parents were already doing the morning milking, and said good-by. Then he headed out. He was anxious to get going. This would probably be his last chance for a good hike in good weather. Besides, this trip was a test for Seth. Not long ago he and Daniel had had an argument about staying the night alone in the woods. Daniel had dared him to do it. Now Seth was going to try.

101

Ever since Seth could remember, he had enjoyed being by himself. He always felt good about himself when he was alone. He had spent the night alone out behind the house many times. But Daniel claimed sleeping out at the pond camp deep in Bear Swamp was a lot different from sleeping out behind the house. Seth wasn't so sure. Well, by tomorrow morning he'd know. He wasn't worried. He could do it. At least he thought he could.

All the hardwood leaves were down except the brown beech leaves, which would hang on all winter, crackling and rasping in the wind. As far as Seth was concerned, this was the most beautiful time of the year. It was a quiet time, a time of clarity and stillness.

Seth's plan was to hike up Raven Hill, then move across the base of Dunn Hill and head down Walker Brook toward the camp he and Daniel had built last summer on the edge of Bear Swamp. He'd spend the night at the camp and come home in the morning—that is, if he could stand it there, all night, alone.

In his backpack he had his cookpots, food for three meals, a ground cloth, his sleeping bag, and a folding saw. Seth always carried a saw instead of a hatchet and a belt knife instead of a pocketknife.

Seth moved through a hardwood grove, his feet wading in the noisy, sun-dried leaves. Then he found the hint of an old logging road. It was fun to find old roads in the woods. Even after they had been unused for fifty or seventy-five years, their imprint remained. There was always that slight two-track depression. Even when there were trees growing in the middle of the road, you could still find the road print winding through the woods. As Seth walked along the old road, he wondered about the last wagon to creak and groan here; he wondered about the first wagon that rolled along that old road.

Soon Seth felt hungry. He found a sunny place near a beech tree where a deer had pawed away the leaves looking for nuts. He eased his backpack off, sat down, and had his lunch.

He ate a peanut butter sandwich, some fresh carrots, and a tomato he'd taken from the windowsill that morning. It was the last tomato, the end of summer. Then he propped his backpack behind his head, stretched himself out on the dry leaves, and ate a couple of cookies.

A red squirrel bounced and chattered across a branch just above his head. The midday sun was warm. A light breeze rattled through the trees and the woods smelled of that delicious, sweet odor of dying leaves. Seth fell asleep.

"Hello!"

"What?" Seth sat up with a frightened start. There was a man standing over him.

"You all right?"

"Ah . . . yes . . . sure."

"Okay," the man said, as he moved away.

For a moment Seth wanted to call the stranger back so they could talk. He suddenly realized that the words he'd said to the stranger were the first words he'd spoken all day. It was good to hear his own voice, good to hear another human voice. But Seth didn't call him back. Instead he sat and watched the stranger move down the road and disappear into the trees.

Seth slipped his pack on and headed down around the base of Dunn Hill. He paused at a little brook, had a drink, and rested. By the looks of the tracks, a big

buck deer had stopped here for a drink the night before.

If Seth had it figured right, he should head west and cross Walker Brook somewhere near its source.

As the sunny hardwood knoll gave way to a stand of dark spruce and fir, Seth could see ahead of him a wet, open place in the softwoods. It was a beaver meadow, an ancient beaver pond now filled with silt. He circled the wet place, found the small trickle of water that was its outlet, and headed downhill. Seth thought this must be the headwaters of Walker Brook. Springs and rills met the brook all along the hillside.

In the woods again, the brook raced through a deep ravine. At one point Seth stood on top of a cliff as high as a house and looked down over the hissing water to where it fell roaring on the boulders below. He tried not to think about falling.

As he descended the mountainside, the brook slowly grew.

Carefully Seth climbed down toward the swamp. Every footrest, every handhold had to be right, exactly right. Slowly, slowly, down he climbed.

Now in the deep softwoods on the edge of the swamp, Seth could see the lean-to he and Daniel had built last summer.

The camp was in pretty good shape. A few minor repairs, a little cleaning up, and everything would be tidy. Seth dumped his backpack on the ground and set to work. He uncovered the salt and sugar he and

Daniel had sealed tight in canning jars and stashed there during the summer. They had also left a coffee-can-and-coat-hanger tea pail on a nail. There was a mouse nest in it.

The stone fireplace they'd built on a sandbar in the brook was the perfect place to cook this time of year. October was a dry time, the fire season. A fire on a sandbar was safe. Seth would keep the fire small, as he always did—a cooking fire.

He walked down the brook to where it entered the swamp, to the beaver dam where he and Daniel had fished last spring.

As he walked out on the beaver dam, a great blue heron rose awkwardly out of the cattails and croaked away over the treetops.

"Sorry," Seth said, as the bird disappeared.

Then he saw a beaver surface near the beaver house at the center of the pond. Maybe it was the same beaver that swam past the canoe last spring. It was like seeing an old friend.

Seth stood on the beaver dam, remembering last spring's fishing trip, remembering the big trout. Then he wandered back to camp, poking here and there along the way. It was good to be back.

After he made the few necessary repairs and gathered wood for the fire, he took the ground cloth from his backpack and spread it out inside the lean-to. Then he unrolled his sleeping bag. He reached inside his backpack for his cookpots and food. He pawed around. He opened the bag wider and looked inside. They weren't there. How could that be? He remembered checking twice, as he always did, when he packed. He was sure he had put them in. Or at least he thought he was sure.

Seth began talking to himself. "Idiot! All the times you've gone camping, you've never done this! And now, when you're out here in this forsaken place overnight alone for the first time. . . ."

Seth was more irritated than frightened. He knew he could find something to eat in the woods, but it was getting late and he was hungry and tired.

There was no one to take the blame, no one but himself, and no point in any moaning. He'd made a mistake, and he'd have to live with it. But he'd have to live with it quickly. It was getting dark.

Focus

1. Seth's camping trip involved a test. What was the test?
2. On the road to the camp, Seth met a man. What did Seth think about talking to him?
3. What was the camp like? Give three details.
4. Seth and William Cottonwood may be very much alike. What did each one do that would make you think so?
5. What do you think Seth will do next?

Last Days of Brightness, Part 2

DAVID BUDBILL

Seth slipped his empty backpack on and headed for the swamp. He remembered that last spring he'd smelled mint and wintergreen in the swamp. That would make good tea. And there were cattails. Cattail roots were good boiled, sort of like potatoes.

Seth reached the spot where the heron had been and pulled up about a dozen cattails, cut off their knobby, brown roots with his belt knife, and put them in his pack. Then, after wandering around a bit, he noticed a familiar-looking bush with glossy, round, deep-green leaves. He picked a leaf, crushed it between his fingers, and sniffed. Wintergreen. He picked a good handful and stuffed it in his shirt pocket.

Seth continued across a beaver dam and foraged on

the far side of the pond. Then on a small hummock he saw something else he recognized. Cranberries. They would be much too bitter to eat alone, but if he could find the last of some blackberries or raspberries somewhere, the two together would be delicious.

Finding blackberries or raspberries wasn't as easy as Seth had imagined, and he was not the first one who had come upon the blackberries he finally found. The bushes were beaten down, their stalks stripped of leaves as well as berries. It was the sure sign of a bear. Bears weren't very dainty when they ate berries, and there were only a few berries left. They were old and dry, but they would do. Seth picked them carefully, wondering how a bear could stand all those thorns in its paws and mouth.

Wintergreen for tea, cranberries and blackberries for dessert, cattail roots for potatoes—too bad he didn't have some meat. Then it dawned on him. In his first-aid kit he always carried a few yards of fishing line and a couple of hooks. Seth cut an alder branch and made a crude fishing pole. Now the only thing between him and a couple of trout was some bait. With his belt knife he began digging in a rotten log. Nothing. Then in another log and another. Still nothing. Finally he found what he was looking for: grubs—tiny, white, wormlike creatures, with little brown, ugly heads, about the size of his thumbnail. They were good trout bait. But he had only two. If he was careful, two grubs

could mean two trout.

They did.

Seth built a fire, then washed the tea pail and peeled the cattail roots. After the fire had settled to coals and the cattail roots were boiling in their water, Seth gutted the two trout and skewered them on a green, forked stick. He roasted them slowly, turning them again and again over the hot coals. When the trout curled and began to fall from the stick, he ate.

Seth had forgotten his anger. He was so involved in what he was doing that he hadn't noticed that the sun had slipped behind the mountains. Now it was rapidly growing dark. He put some wood on the fire and let it grow a little.

He took off his boots and crawled inside the lean-to. He propped his head on his boots and pack and watched the quiet fire brighten as dark slipped down around the trees. The firelight bounced across the boulder on the far side of the brook where last spring a chipmunk had sat and eaten part of Daniel's sandwich.

Suddenly Seth was afraid. It was dark, dark. The big trees were tall shadows now. It seemed to Seth that they all were leaning down on him, as if to do him harm. And everywhere he looked he thought he saw creatures, strange, unknown creatures in the trees. They were watching him, watching him and waiting. He heard a stick crack off in the woods. Then right behind the lean-to, just a few feet away, there was a grinding, chewing sound.

He put more wood on the fire.

He was tired. It was time to sleep. He'd stay up to watch the fire just a little longer. He found himself staring at the firelight. It held him in a warm, bright circle, making a room of light for him, a place to live the night. And beyond that place, just a step away, there was the unknown dark, the wild and frightening dark.

Then a barred owl somewhere up on Dunn Hill began calling to the night. Seth could hear him saying, "Alone. Alone. Alone. A-l-o-n-e." Seth had always loved to hear owls calling in the night, but now that soft, round call made him feel even more lonely, even more afraid. The owl called again, "Alone. A-l-o-n-e."

Seth said to himself, almost in a whimper, "Me, too."

Now Seth was fighting to stay awake. He added a couple of good-sized logs to the fire to make more light. He was cold. He climbed, fully dressed, into his

111

sleeping bag. The sleeping bag warmed him and made it even harder to stay awake. The owl called again. Then the moon rose, orange and huge, through the branches of the softwood trees. He fell asleep.

Sometime during the night, Seth didn't know exactly when, he awoke. The fire had died down to coals. Straight overhead, the black, bowl-like, cloudless sky held a full moon. Seth could see the moon's face, its eyes and nose, its round, open mouth.

The moon filled the woods with cold, silver light. It cast sharp black shadows everywhere. It lit the brook white. It was as if Seth had been carried away in a dream to another, unknown place, to an enormous, silent, black-and-white room, the lonely night-room of the earth. The world was still, as if it were dead. There was no wind, no sound, except the brook's quiet hiss.

Then somewhere between where Seth lay and his warm house five miles to the east, a shrill, chilling cry rose over the earth. First one, then two, then three howls rising and falling, rising and falling. Then the short, sharp barks. Then the howls again. Coyotes. Then the answer came from somewhere behind him, nearby in the swamp.

Now Seth wanted to sleep. Sleep was the only place left to hide.

Quietly he crept out of the lean-to and added wood to the fire. He got back into his sleeping bag quickly. Then he lay back and listened to those unseen wanderers of the dark.

The next time Seth woke, the moon was down, and the sky toward the east was slowly turning pink. Now the forest was loud and alive again, filled to overflowing with the glad morning song of birds. The chickadee was singing, the myrtle warbler was singing, the junco and the cedar waxwing and a dozen other birds Seth couldn't recognize. They were all alive and singing in the dawn. Seth felt like singing, too.

He climbed out of his sleeping bag, cold and happy. The rising sun washed away the last bits of night. He had made it! He had made it through the night.

Seth started a new fire, then washed his face and rinsed his mouth in the cold water of the brook. For the first time Seth really understood why birds sing so joyously at dawn.

He had known all along that no harm would come to him in the night forest. He knew those coyotes were interested in mice, not people. But what his head knew and what his stomach felt were two very different things.

He chuckled to himself. Daniel had been right. A night in the forest wasn't at all like a night in the back-yard. But he had done it, and he felt proud. No, pride wasn't exactly it. He just felt good, good about himself. He saw himself and the woods and its animals in a way he never had before.

Seth scraped together a breakfast of trout and a big

pail of wintergreen tea. He rolled and packed the ground cloth and sleeping bag. He doused the fire, put away the salt and sugar, washed the tea pail, and hung it back on its nail.

When he was a few yards from the camp, he stopped and looked back. He felt alive, more alive than he ever had before. Then he laughed out loud and said, "I did it!"

Focus

1. How can you tell that Seth was able to identify eatable plants without anyone's help?
2. Seth had stayed at the camp many times. Why was he afraid this time?
3. Seth woke up in the middle of the night. Tell three things that he saw or felt.
4. After his night out, how did Seth feel about himself?

During his night in the woods, Seth ate cattail roots and drank wintergreen tea. Are "weeds" really useful plants?

What Good Is a Weed? ROBERT H. WRIGHT

Few things are so unappreciated as weeds. Farmers, gardeners, and homeowners fight a constant battle against weeds. They spray weeds with poisons, chop them with hoes, and cut them with machines.

What's so bad about a weed? Weeds are disliked because they grow in places where people don't want them. When a violet grows in a cornfield, it is usually called a weed. But when it grows in the woods it is called a wildflower.

The sunflower is another plant that can be either a weed or a flower. It can also be a crop. Farmers sometimes plant fields of sunflowers for their seeds. But if a sunflower starts to grow in a soybean field, it is a weed. When planted in a flower garden, it becomes a flower.

Weeds are important. They supply food for animals. Some weeds have seeds and berries that birds eat. The leaves of other weeds are eaten by insects, rabbits, cattle, and deer. Meadow mice and gophers eat the roots of some weeds.

Even weeds with a bad taste or prickly spines are important. Prickles and spines protect small animals from their enemies. Small animals can hide between the sharp spines. They also protect the sprouts of other plants that might be eaten by grazing animals.

Many weeds protect the soil from wind and rain. Their roots make tiny openings in the soil. These openings let rain soak in. If the water rushed over the land, it would make gullies and wash away the topsoil. Topsoil is needed for growing crops.

In earlier days people often ate weeds themselves. Many weeds, such as sunflowers, dandelions, and cattails, were used as food by Native Americans and early settlers. When their crops failed, pioneers were grateful for the food they got from weeds.

Weeds were often used as medicines, too. Some of the old weed remedies contain chemicals that are useful in modern medicines. One example is snakeroot, which grows in India. It was used for centuries as a cure for snakebite. Snakeroot is still used today in making medicines.

117

In the past, people had many uses for weeds other than as medicines and food. They used weeds in making their homes, their furniture, their toys, and their tools. Cattail leaves were used to make woven seats for chairs. The fluff from the ripe cattail heads was used for stuffing pillows.

An example of a useful weed is the dandelion. For centuries, people have used it for both food and medicine. Medicines made from it were used to treat illnesses like flu. Dandelions are rich in vitamin A and C.

The most useful parts of the dandelion are the leaves. In the spring, when the leaves are tender, some people cook them in water. The leaves are usually served as spinach is served and even taste a little like spinach.

The leaves are not the only part of the dandelion that is eaten. Even the yellow flowers can be eaten if picked while they are still buds. The roots can also be eaten. The young roots are cooked like parsnips. The older ones are roasted until they crumble into small pieces. The roasted roots can be used to make a hot drink that is like coffee.

Many people used to eat dandelions for dinner. The dandelion has even helped save some people from starving. Once a plague of grasshoppers ate all the green plants on an island. The people who lived there survived on dandelion roots.

Today people do not eat dandelions as they once

did. One reason is the danger from sprays and fertilizers. Small amounts of spray often settle on wild plants, thus making them unsafe to eat. Be sure never to eat plants that may have been sprayed with dangerous chemicals.

Dandelions also provide food for insects. Every part of the plant is eaten by insects of one kind or another. The pollen and nectar of the blossoms are gathered by honeybees and bumblebees. Some rodents eat the roots.

Wherever dandelions grow, their white fuzzy seeds can be seen floating through the air. Because they have floating seeds dandelions have been able to spread around the world.

Children sometimes blow the fuzz from a dandelion seed ball. Then they make up stories about the number of seeds left on the ball.

Dandelions are like many other green plants. Sometimes they can be useful, and sometimes they are just weeds.

Focus

1. Why do some people dislike weeds?
2. Tell a few ways that weeds can be useful.
3. Why don't people today eat dandelions as people did in the past?
4. How did Seth in "Last Days of Brightness" use wild plants?

LIFE SKILL: Health and Safety Labels

Have you ever had your own garden? If so, you may have used sprays and fertilizers. Sprays help control harmful pests. Fertilizers are special plant foods that help plants grow.

The same products that help plants can hurt people and animals. So most sprays and fertilizers have labels like the one at the top of the next page. The labels warn against harmful chemicals.

Many other useful items have chemicals that can harm people. Soaps can harm people if they are swallowed. Paints and medicines can be harmful if they are not used properly. For these reasons it is important to read the label before using any product. The label will tell you what to do. It will also tell you what not to do.

Look again at the first label on the next page. A label tells you the name of the product. What is the name of this one? What word next catches your eye? What is the word in large black type? What does it mean? Now look at the second label on the next page. It is from a can of paint thinner. Here you should notice the words **CAUTION** and **WARNING.** What do they mean?

CAUTION, WARNING, DANGER, and **POISON** are key words to watch for. These words are usually printed larger than the other words on the label. The directions following these words will tell you what not to do.

Many labels tell you what to do if something goes wrong. Others give you a telephone number to call in an emergency. If you think that someone is in serious danger, call a doctor right away.

CLEAN GARDEN WEED KILLER

WARNING: Harmful if swallowed. Do not get in eyes, on skin, or on clothing. Do not breathe fumes. In case of eye contact, wash eyes with water. Wash hands well after using product. Apply this product only as label directs. Keep away from children.

PAINT THINNER

DIRECTIONS: To thin paint add small amount of thinner and stir. If paint is still too thick add thinner as necessary. To clean brushes, soak them in thinner until they are clean; then wash brushes thoroughly with soap and water. **CAUTION:** Keep thinner off skin and away from eyes. It may cause irritation. Wash hands thoroughly after use.

WARNING: For external use only. Do not take internally. If swallowed, call a doctor.

On a separate piece of paper, answer these questions.

1. How are some chemicals both helpful and harmful?
2. Why is it important to read the label before you use a product?
3. What are some key words to look for before using a product?
4. Make a list of products that you think have danger warnings.
5. Why should harmful products be kept away from children?

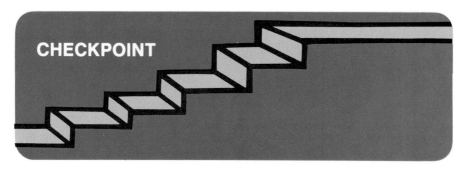

CHECKPOINT

Vocabulary:
Word
Identification
Below are four vocabulary words. Next to each word are three short definitions. On your paper write each vocabulary word and its definition.

1. shrill: (type of pen, piercing sound, fancy border)
2. crude: (clever, family fight, natural state)
3. descended: (went down, abandoned, cured)
4. depression: (lower place, cliff, happy mood)

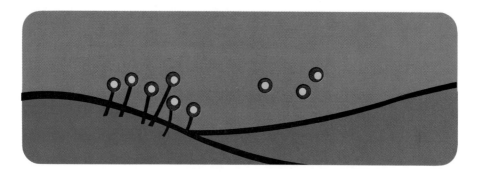

Comprehension:
Main
Idea
The main idea of a paragraph gives a short summary of the paragraph. One sentence is usually enough. Read the following paragraph about dandelions. Then write the sentence from the list below that tells the main idea of the paragraph.

Not everyone thinks that dandelions are bad. Some people think that dandelions are useful or even pretty. Dandelions can look pretty growing in a field. The yellow color looks cheerful mixed with green plants. Sometimes dandelions are used in foods or drinks.

Dandelions can even be worn. Some children like to make dandelion necklaces or bracelets. Other children, if they find dandelions that are fuzzy and white, will make wishes and blow on the fuzz. They watch the fuzz spread through the air and hope that their wishes come true.

5. Dandelions
Some dandelions are used in foods or drinks.
Dandelions can be controlled with sprays.
Some people like dandelions and even use them.

Complete each sentence below with a word from the list. Write the completed sentences on your paper.

Decoding:
Prefix *in-*,
Suffix *-ic*

inspect   allergy   inhale   scenic   respect
inhalant   scenery   spectator   allergic   inspection

6. Seth likes to_____the scent of mint and wintergreen.
7. The hiker stopped to view the_____landscape.
8. Alice will_____the plants for traces of poisonous sprays.
9. Barbara stays away from weeds because she is_____to them.

A special violet growing in a cornfield is called a weed. And a yagua in Puerto Rico makes a special kind of day . . . a yagua day.

YAGUA DAYS

CRUZ MARTEL

It was drizzling steadily in the city. From the doorway of her parents' store, Maria Riera watched a car splash the sidewalk.

School had ended for the summer two days ago, and for two days it had rained. Maria wanted to play in East River Park, but with so much rain about the only thing a girl could do was watch cars splash by.

Of course she could help her father. Maria enjoyed working in her parents' store. But today she would rather be in the park. She watched another car spray past. The rain began to fall harder.

Mail carrier Marta sloshed in, slapping water off her hat. She smiled. "What's happening, Maria? Why do you have such a long face?"

"Rainy days are terrible days."

"No—they're wonderful days. They're yagua days!"

"Stop teasing, Marta. What's a yagua day?"

"This day is a yagua day," she answered.

Maria asked again, "What's a yagua day?"

Maria's mother and father came over to join the conversation.

"Hello, Marta. You look wet."

"I feel wetter. But it's a wonderful feeling. It's a yagua-day feeling!"

"So you've been telling Maria about yagua days?"

"Yes! Here's a letter for you."

Maria's father read the letter. "Good news! My brother Ulise wants Mami, Maria, and me to visit him on his plantation for two weeks."

"You haven't been to Puerto Rico in years," said Marta.

"Maria's never been there," replied her mother. "We can ask my brother to take care of the store. Maria will meet her family in the mountains at last."

Maria clapped her hands. "Puerto Rico! Who cares about the rain!"

Marta smiled. "Maybe you'll even have a few yagua days. Good-bye, and have fun!"

Maria wondered, "What is a yagua day?"

Two weeks later Uncle Ulise met them at the airport in Ponce.*

*pōn′sā

"Welcome to Puerto Rico, Maria."

Stocky Uncle Ulise had tiny blue eyes in a round, red face, and big, strong arms. Maria, excited after her first plane ride, hugged Uncle Ulise even harder than Uncle Ulise hugged her.

"Come, we'll drive to Corral Viejo."* He winked at Maria's father. "I'm sorry you didn't arrive yesterday. Yesterday was a wonderful yagua day."

Maria looked at her uncle in surprise. "You know about yagua days too, Uncle Ulise?"

"Sure. They're my favorite days."

"But wouldn't today be a good yagua day?"

"The worst. The sun's out!"

In an old jeep, they wound up into the mountains.

"Look!" said Uncle Ulise, pointing at a river flowing over rocks. "Your mother and father and I played in that river when we were children."

They bounced up a hill to a cluster of bright houses. Many people were outside.

"This is your family, Maria," said Uncle Ulise.

Everyone crowded around the jeep. Old and young people. Blond-, brown-, and black-haired people. Dark-skinned and light-skinned people. Blue-eyed, brown-eyed, and green-eyed people. Maria had not known there were so many people in her family.

Uncle Ulise's wife Carmen hugged Maria and kissed both her cheeks. She was taller than Uncle Ulise and very thin. Aunt Carmen's straight mouth never

127

*cō räl′ vē ā′hō

smiled—but her eyes certainly did.

The whole family sat under wide trees and ate rice with peas, roast pork, vegetables, salads of avocado and tomato, and Puerto Rican dumplings.

Maria talked and sang until her voice turned to a squeak. She ate until her stomach almost popped a pants' button.

Afterward she fell asleep under a big mosquito net before the sun had even gone down behind the mountains.

In the morning Uncle Ulise called out, "Maria, everyone ate all the food in the house. Let's get more."

"From a store?"

"No, from my plantation on the mountain."

"You drive a tractor and plow on the mountain?"

Aunt Carmen smiled with her eyes. "We don't need tractors and plows on our plantation."

"I don't understand."

"Come on. You'll see."

Maria and her parents, Aunt Carmen, and Uncle Ulise hiked up the mountain beside a splashy stream.

Near the top they walked through groves of fruit trees.

"Long ago your grandfather planted these trees," Maria's mother said. "Now Aunt Carmen and Uncle Ulise pick what they need for themselves, or want to give away, or want to sell in Ponce."

"Let's work!" said Aunt Carmen.

Sitting on her father's shoulders, Maria picked oranges.

Swinging a hooked stick, she pulled down *mangós*.

Whipping a bamboo pole with a knife tied to the end, she chopped breadfruit from a tall tree.

Digging with a machete, she uncovered *nãmes*.*

Finally, gripping a very long pole, she struck down coconuts.

"How do we get all the food down the mountain?" she asked.

"Watch," said Aunt Carmen. She whistled loudly.

Maria saw a patch of white moving in the trees. A horse with a golden mane appeared.

Uncle Ulise fed him some fruit. The horse twitched his ears and munched the delicious fruit loudly.

"Palomo will help us carry all the fruit and vegetables we've picked," Maria's mother said.

Back at the house, Maria gave Palomo another piece of fruit.

"He'll go back up to the plantation now," her father said. "He's got all he wants to eat there."

Uncle Ulise rubbed his knee.

"What's the matter?" asked Maria's mother.

"My knee. It always hurts just before rain comes."

Maria looked at the cloudless sky. "But it's not going to rain."

"Yes, it will. My knee never lies. It'll rain tonight. Maybe tomorrow. When it does, it'll be a yagua day!"

129

*nyä′mā

In the morning Maria, waking up cozy under her mosquito net, heard rain banging on the metal roof and tree frogs beeping like tiny car horns.

She jumped out of bed and got a big surprise. Her mother and father and Uncle Ulise and Aunt Carmen were on the porch wearing bathing suits.

"Come on, Maria," her father said. "It's a wonderful yagua day. Put on your bathing suit!"

In the forest she heard shouts and swishing noises

in the rain.

Racing into a clearing, she saw boys and girls shooting down a runway of grass, then disappearing over a rock ledge.

Uncle Ulise picked up a canoelike object from the grass. "This is a yagua, Maria. It fell from this palm tree."

"And this is what we do with it," said her father. He ran, then belly-flopped on the yagua. He skimmed down the grass, sailed up into the air, and vanished over the ledge. Her mother found another yagua and did the same.

"Papi! Mami!"

Uncle Ulise laughed. "Don't worry, Maria. They won't hurt themselves. The river is down there. There is a pool beneath the ledge. The rain turns the grass butter-slick so you can zip into the water. That's what makes it a yagua day. Come and join us!"

That day Maria found out what fun a yagua day is!

Focus

1. Why did Maria go to Puerto Rico?
2. How were Maria's surroundings in Puerto Rico different from her surroundings at home?
3. How did Uncle Ulise get food for everyone to eat? What were some of the foods?
4. Describe a yagua day. Give three or four details.
5. How did Maria's feelings about rainy days change?

131

In "Yagua Days" Maria learns that children in Puerto Rico can have fun outdoors, even when it rains. In "The Visitor," Roberta learns that the outdoors is not always fun.

THE VISITOR
KARLEEN BRADFORD

"There go some more mallards flying south, Dad. Winter's coming for sure." Roberta stood at the big picture window in her living room, looking out across Georgian Bay towards Lake Huron itself. A "V" of ducks was flying low across the water. The lights of an oil tanker could just be seen in the gathering dusk. It was early November. Snow had not yet come to this part of Ontario, but it was very cold and raining heavily.

"Br-r-r! I'm glad I'm not out there." Roberta shivered as she climbed the stairs and got ready for bed.

During the night the temperature dropped even more. When Roberta went out early the next morning, everything was covered with glistening ice. Even their own little cove had frozen over. As she walked towards it to investigate, she cupped her mouth in her hands and breathed hard to warm up her fingers. Her breath came out in frosty little puffs. She hopped a few steps to keep her toes from freezing. As she drew near a marshy spot by the shore, she saw something dark

133

among the reeds. "That's funny," she said out loud, "that looks like a duck!"

She walked up to it curiously, expecting with each step she took that it would fly away. It lay perfectly still, however, and when she reached it, she could see why. Its body and head were covered in greasy black oil, and it was frozen fast in the ice. At first Roberta thought it was dead, but when she touched it, it made a feeble attempt to fly. Gently Roberta slid her hands underneath the duck and started freeing the feathers, one by one. The duck struggled from time to time as Roberta worked, but it was growing weaker. When she finally had it loose, she cradled it carefully in both hands and ran back to the house.

"Mom, look what I've found!" she cried as she kicked the back door with her foot. Roberta's mother opened the door and she rushed straight through to the kitchen. "It's a mallard, Mom, and it's nearly dead. I found it frozen in the ice."

"What in the world has it got all over it?" her mother asked, looking at the duck in alarm.

"Oil," Roberta answered in disgust. "Some big globs have been coming ashore since the tanker spill last week."

"What are you going to do with it, Roberta?" Her mother grabbed a cloth and started mopping at the dripping oil and water on the floor.

"I'll have to clean it off somehow, if it's going to

live, but that's an awfully hard job. Remember that program we saw on television the other night? It was about those people who were using detergents to remove oil from seabirds they had rescued off the coast of England. They said that a weak mixture of detergent and warm water worked best. It's after you get them cleaned up that you have to watch out, though," she continued. "If they don't get their natural oil back, they still won't live. Their feathers won't be waterproof, and they'll either get waterlogged and drown, or freeze to death."

Roberta held the duck while her mother mixed some dishwashing liquid and warm water in a large bucket. Then, holding the duck as firmly and as carefully as she could, Roberta lowered it into the water. 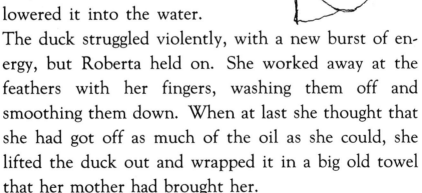 The duck struggled violently, with a new burst of energy, but Roberta held on. She worked away at the feathers with her fingers, washing them off and smoothing them down. When at last she thought that she had got off as much of the oil as she could, she lifted the duck out and wrapped it in a big old towel that her mother had brought her.

"Let's take it and put it down in that pen that Dad made for the Mitchells' dog when we kept him last summer," she said. "It's good and big and has a neat little house at one end that I can fill with straw for it."

In a short time, the duck was nestled into the bed of straw and was lying quietly. "I guess that's all we can do for it now," Roberta said, but she continued to crouch down and peer in at the duck through the wire.

The next morning Roberta was up and out at the duck pen before her mother and father were awake. She knelt down to look. The duck was lying as she had left it, the dish of water beside it still full. The corn she had scattered around was untouched. Roberta walked slowly back to the house.

At school that day, she found it hard to keep her mind on her work. When the three-thirty bell rang, she was the first one out. She ran all the way home and arrived at the duck pen out of breath. The duck was up and pecking at the corn! As Roberta watched, it drank a bit of water and then settled down to groom its feathers. First it poked sharply with its bill at the oil sac hidden beneath the feathers on its back, just under the curl of its dark green tail. Then it drew its bill up around the curl, to get the bill well coated with oil. Next it preened its feathers carefully, one by one, coating them again with its own natural, weather-

and waterproofing oil. Roberta watched in delight for a few moments and then ran for the house.

"It's going to be all right, Mom! Mom! It's really going to be all right!" Roberta's mother came running out, and together they watched the duck working away at its feathers.

Two weeks later, it was a very different duck that strutted up and down the pen, quacking angrily for its corn whenever Roberta was late. The dull and bedraggled feathers had recovered their sheen, and the duck had put on weight. The brown and grey body shone sleekly. The proud green head gleamed in the weak wintry sunlight. The white around its neck and the bright blue patches on its wings stood out brightly and clearly.

"Doesn't the duck look great, Dad?" Roberta beamed as she showed it off to her father one afternoon. "It comes running to me as soon as it sees me in the morning, and it almost eats out of my hand. Pretty soon it'll be so tame it'll probably follow me around like a real pet!"

"Roberta," her father answered seriously, "you're going to have to let the duck go very soon."

Roberta looked away quickly. "I know," she answered, with a sudden hollow feeling in her chest. "I've been thinking about that." She turned away from the pen and scuffed at the gravel under her feet.

The sun went behind a cloud at that moment and

Roberta pulled her collar around her ears. The wind suddenly had a colder bite to it, and the smell of snow was in the air.

"If we wait any longer, it will be too late for the duck to fly south," Roberta's father continued quietly. "We've got to let it loose before it forgets completely how to fend for itself."

"I know," Roberta answered again slowly, "but how can we be sure that it'll survive? We don't even know for certain that its feathers are completely water-proofed again."

"We'll move the pen down to the shore so that most of the run is in the water. It's light enough so that if we each lift one side we can walk it down slowly, with the duck still inside it. Then we'll see how it does in the water."

The next day they came out to check again on the duck. It was swimming happily around in the small square of water, seemingly none the worse for it. As they watched, another "V" of ducks flew by, calling to each other. The duck in the pen seemed to hear and understand. It grew more and more excited, swimming back and forth and answering the passing ducks. As they disappeared out over the bay, it flew against the wire mesh, beating its wings desperately in its efforts to get out.

"We're going to have to let it go, Roberta," her father said.

Roberta turned to look at her father. She felt almost as desperate as the duck. "It seems to be all right again, Dad," she said, "but how can we be sure?"

"We can't, Roberta, but you've done your best. There's nothing more you can do for it."

Roberta reached for the latch of the pen, hesitated a moment, then flung it open. In a flurry of feathers, the duck was out and flying—a bit shakily at first—but soon its wing beats were strong and steady. It flew straight down the bay, heading south, and then it was gone.

Roberta stood watching after the duck for a long time. When she became aware of the first fine snow driving against her face, she hunched her shoulders and turned away. Her duck was free once more. Free to live or free to die—she didn't know. But she had done her best.

Focus

1. What did Roberta find when she went out on the first cold morning?
2. What did Roberta do to help the duck?
3. How did the duck waterproof itself?
4. Roberta felt uneasy about letting the duck go free. Why?
5. At the end of the story, how did Roberta feel about herself? How was she like Seth in "Last Days of Brightness"?

STUDY SKILL: Guide Words

To clean oil off the duck, Roberta used a mixture of warm water and detergent. Do you know what detergent is? If you did not know the meaning of the word, you might look it up in the dictionary.

You know that the words in a dictionary are arranged in alphabetical order. So of course you would look for *detergent* among the words beginning with "d." But you can waste time flipping through the "d" pages looking for your word. Guide words to help you find words quickly.

The opposite page is like a page in a dictionary. Look at the top of the page. The two words in heavy black type are guide words. The guide word on the left is the same as the first word on the page. The guide word on the right shows the last word on the page. All the other words on the page are listed in alphabetical order from *destiny* to *dew*. Is *detergent* on this page?

Use the sample page from the dictionary to answer these questions.

1. What information about the dictionary page do the guide words give you?
2. Why would you expect the word *detergent* to be on the page that had *destiny* and *dew* for guide words?
3. Which words on the dictionary page are in heavy type? Explain how heavy type helps you to find words.

des·ti·ny (des′ tə nē) *noun.* 1. what becomes of someone or something; one's fate or fortune. 2. what will happen in spite of efforts to change or prevent it.

de·stroy (di stroi′) *verb.* to ruin, break or make useless. **destroyed, destroying.**

de·tach (di tach′) *verb.* 1. to separate or remove. 2. to send away on special duty. **detached, detaching.**

de·tail (di tāl′ or dē′ tāl) *noun.* 1. a small unimportant part. 2. a small group selected and sent for special duty. —*verb.* 1. to deal with small things one by one. 2. to tell something fully, even the small unimportant parts. **detailed, detailing.**

de·tain (di tān′) *verb.* 1. to hold back; delay. 2. to hold as prisoner. **detained, detaining.**

de·ter·gent (di tėr′ jənt) *noun.* a substance used for cleaning; a chemical compound that can dissolve oil.

de·ter·mi·na·tion (di tėr′ mə nā′ shən) *noun.* 1. a strong sense of purpose. 2. a settlement of some problem; a decision.

de·throne (di thrōn′) *verb.* to remove from the throne; to take away ruling power. **dethroned, dethroning.**

det·o·nate (det′ n āt) *verb.* to set off an explosion. **detonated, detonating.**

de·tour (dē′ tu̇r) *noun.* a roundabout way; off the main course. —*verb.* to use a detour.

de·vel·op (di vel′əp) *verb.* 1. to grow or come into being. 2. to make or become bigger or better. **developed, developing.**

dew (dü or dyü) *noun.* 1. moisture from the air that condenses on cool surfaces like grass. 2. anything moist, refreshing, or pure.

CHECKPOINT

Read the paragraph below about how Roberta rescued the mallard. From the list choose the one word that best completes each sentence. Write the completed paragraph on your paper.

desperate	mallard	investigate	groves
strutted	detergent	palm	conversation

One morning Roberta decided to __(1)__ the cove near her home. She spotted a __(2)__ covered in black oil and frozen in the ice. The frightened bird seemed __(3)__ as it tried to fly but didn't have the strength. Roberta freed the mallard and took it to her house. To remove the oil she washed the bird with warm water and __(4)__ . A few weeks later the duck __(5)__ around its pen the way a healthy bird would. Roberta was happy that the duck was well.

The first sentence below is a main idea statement from "The Visitor." Following the main idea are six details, but only four of them support the main idea. Write on your paper the four details that support the main idea.

Comprehension: Supporting Details

6. People can help save lives of seabirds that have been hurt by oil.

   a. Roberta freed the oil-stained duck from the ice.

   b. Roberta washed the duck in warm water and detergent.

   c. Roberta liked to look at the duck.

   d. Roberta fed corn to the weak duck.

   e. Roberta put the duck near water so it could fly south with the other ducks.

   f. Roberta watched the duck swim.

Guide words can help you find a word in the dictionary. Write the following list of dictionary entry words on your paper. Next to each word write the guide words that would appear on the page with that entry word.

Study Skill: Guide Words

Entry Words	Guide Words
7. mosquito	lecture—legalize
8. peer	moan—mope
9. mane	more—mother
10. ledge	peek—peg
11. model	manage—map

143

Roberta saved a mallard's life by herself. Some animal problems need the attention of special people. That's when veterinarians are welcome.

Animals Need Doctors, Too

HOWARD J. LEBOWITZ

Animals need help just as people do. The animal may be a stray dog, or a beached whale, or an oil-stained duck. Without help these animals would probably not live. Most people help animals as best they can, but sometimes a doctor has to be called.

Doctors who take care of animals are called veterinarians, or vets for short. Vets give animals check-ups and treat them when they are sick.

Vets are people who like working with animals. Many vets start their careers early. As children and young people they read books about animals in school and might even have worked in pet stores. After high school people who want to be vets go to college and usually study science. After college they go to veterinary school for four years. In veterinary school students learn how to treat animals. They also try to decide what kind of animal work they want to do.

There are different kinds of animal workers. Some

vets take care of pets such as dogs and cats. Some vets work in zoos. Some work on farms. A few work in animal parks or national forests.

Pet Care

Pets are common in families that live in the city. Veterinarians who take care of pets usually work in animal hospitals. In one day the animal hospital vet might help a rabbit with an ear infection, a cat with a wounded paw, and a dog with a broken leg. Pet vets also try to prevent animal sickness. One way to do that is to give vaccinations.

City vets help pet owners know how to care for their animals. Some questions that people ask vets are: How should I get rid of my pet's fleas and worms? How much should my pet weigh? What is the best food for my pet?

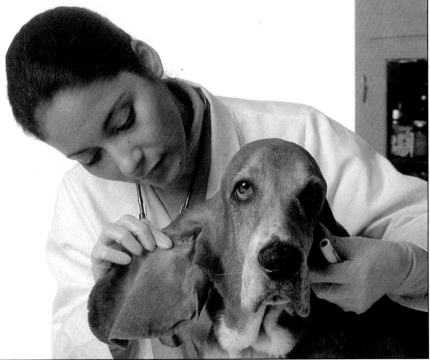

Zoo Animals

Zoo vets care for animals that are not as common as pets. Zoos have all kinds of interesting animals, including zebras, spiders, and rhinos. Because the animals stay right in the zoo, the vet gets to know them. Each day the vet goes on "rounds." That means going around to check on all the animals. On daily rounds the vet talks to the keepers and asks if there are any problems.

Sometimes there are problems. A keeper might say that a snake does not look well. The vet then checks the snake. Can you imagine looking down a sick snake's throat? Where do you think the throat ends

and the stomach begins? If the snake has a stomach infection, the vet can give it some medicine. In a few days the snake will be healthy again.

Sometimes the vet has to bring the sick animal to the zoo's hospital. Say an alligator with a sore foot needs X-rays. To take the X-ray the keeper puts on heavy gloves, tapes the alligator's jaws closed, and brings the animal to the hospital in the zoo's ambulance. After X-rays, the vet decides that there is nothing seriously wrong with the foot. In a few weeks the alligator is better.

Animals that get sick can infect other animals. A zoo vet has to decide when to put sick animals in the hospital away from other animals. This is called putting them in quarantine. An infection can spread quickly from one animal to another. The sooner a vet can put a sick animal in quarantine, the safer the other animals

will be.

Not all of the zoo vet's work has to do with sick animals. The health of new animals has to be checked before they're brought to the zoo. Animals that are sent from foreign countries are shipped by plane in large crates. When they arrive the vet goes to the airport to make some tests and sign papers that confirm that the animals are healthy. Then the crates are loaded onto trucks and driven to the zoo. There is usually a lot of excitement when new animals arrive at the zoo. Would you be surprised to see a truck going by your school carrying two baby elephants in large crates?

Zoo animals vary greatly in size. One day a zoo vet may have to check the heartbeat of a whale with special electronic equipment. The next day he might have to bandage the leg of a hummingbird. Most bird problems have to do with the wings or the feet. On these parts of the body birds may be nonresistant to infections. These infections can be treated with salves.

There are animals in the zoo that are not as delicate as birds. Some animals are big and dangerous. Bears, for example, can be dangerous. What would you do if you had to treat a sick bear? Before getting very close a vet will put a bear to sleep with a drug. The drug doesn't hurt the bear. After a few minutes the animal will wake up. While the bear is asleep, the vet can examine it without any nonsense.

Wild Animal Parks

Some vets work in wild animal parks. These parks are like zoos except that the animals roam free while the visitors stay on special paths. The land in these animal

parks is like the land in places in the world where the animals are found. So the animals feel at home. There are large wild animal parks in Texas, Florida, Indiana, and Alberta, Canada.

The vets in the wild animal parks take care of the animals just as zoo vets take care of zoo animals. The vet may feed a baby hippo by hand, or give medicine to a deer. The vets pay close attention to the food the animals eat. An animal's diet is important to its health. The parks have huge kitchens where special foods are made. For example, some gorillas don't eat bananas. They like cereal and milk. Many of the other animals eat large "cakes" made of grain, vegetables, yeast, salt, and milk.

Vets at wild animal parks also do research. Doing research means discovering new ideas about a subject. Vets try to discover new and better ways of caring for animals.

Farm Animal Care

Pets, zoo animals, and wild animals are not the only animals that need care. So do farm animals. Doctors who treat farm animals are sometimes called country vets. Country vets treat such animals as cows, horses, chickens, goats, and sheep. Since farms are far apart, the farm vets travel a lot. Some have C.B. radios in their cars so that they can find out about emergencies. One day a vet was called on his C.B. radio. A cow had

149

become sick from eating poisonous plants. The vet rushed to the farm, gave the cow an antidote, and saved its life.

A country vet also checks cows that are not sick. The vet makes tests of a cow's milk and sometimes takes blood samples to be sure the cow is healthy. Once in a while a cow may need a pill, such as a vitamin. There is a special tool for giving pills to cows. The vet uses the tool to slide the pill to the back of the cow's throat. Even then the cow might not swallow the pill!

Horses may need treatment, too. The most common problem with horses is lameness. A lame horse can't use its hoof. Sometimes a shot of medicine will be enough to heal the lameness. Sometimes the vet has to

operate on the leg.

Many of the country vet's jobs can be done right on the farm. When a problem is more serious, the animal has to go to the animal hospital. At the hospital the vet can take X-rays and do operations. For example, cows often have stomach problems. Because cows have four stomachs, sometimes one stomach slips out of place. So the vet has to sew it back where it belongs. Cows are always shaky after such an operation, but usually they can go home the next day.

Imagine how the vet feels when patients get well! If you work with animals, you may know that feeling. If you think you'd like to work with animals, try asking people in pet shops, kennels, or animal shelters what kind of work they do there. Or ask veterinarians. You may want to be a vet when you get older. Start early. Learn all you can. There are still not enough vets to care for all the animals.

Focus
1. What is a vet?
2. What are the four kinds of vets that the author tells about?
3. Tell three responsibilities of a zoo vet.
4. How is a wild animal park different from a zoo?
5. Children who think they might want to be veterinarians can start early. What are some things they can do?

All animal problems are not serious. Some are funny.
Here is a true story told by a veterinarian.

SQUIRREL IN A WHAT?

WESLEY A. YOUNG AND GLORIA D. MIKLOWITZ

Dr. Wesley Young is a veterinarian and a former
director of the Los Angeles Zoo. In this story he tells
about an amusing experience that happened while he
was working at the Animal Rescue League.

The phone call came on a busy Saturday at the Animal Rescue League. As I picked it up on its third ring,
I was strapping a splint on a dog's leg. I held the phone
with my shoulder and neck.

I could hear a child crying in the background and
the voices of children rising and falling in disagreement.
I could also hear a musical tone like that of some brass
instrument. Over the noise came the voice of a man
trying to explain an emergency.

" . . . and she has to play in the parade at one
o'clock! It's ten thirty already, and we've tried everything. It won't come out!"

As I tried to digest the information, I reached with
a free hand for some tape, and glanced quickly at the
wall clock. It was ten thirty. The office was full with

the usual weekend clients. A young girl was holding her pet parakeet in its cage. A dog was yelping with pain from wounds that it received in a fight with a cat. Animals were barking, meowing, and chirping.

I nodded to Harry Rolfe, one of the staff of the Rescue League. I returned to my splint work while he took over the call. Harry wrote down an address and headed for the door.

About an hour later, Harry called in. "Say, Doc, I'm in town with a funny problem. The people who called have a daughter who plays the tuba. In fact, she's due to play in the school band this afternoon. It's the only tuba the band has, as a matter of fact. The funny thing is that a squirrel got into the horn, and I can't get it out. I've done everything I could think of. I've blown into it, hollered into it, shaken it, reached into the bell with sticks and wires. The squirrel won't budge. It's nearly noon, Doc, and we're running out of time. What'll I do?"

"Come on now, Harry," I said. "What would a squirrel be doing in a tuba? There's probably something wrong with the horn."

"No, Doc, take my word for it. It's a squirrel, all right. It seems that storm we had last month blew down an old oak tree. A whole family of squirrels became homeless. The tuba player, Jan, found a baby squirrel, and adopted it. She's made a bed for it in her room. She feeds it regularly and takes it everyplace with her. She even keeps the squirrel in her pocket when she practices her tuba."

"Well, what makes everyone so sure the squirrel's in the tuba?"

"For one thing, nobody can find it anywhere around the house," Harry answered.

"Okay, so it got outside," I argued. "A squirrel isn't likely to stay in a house now, is it? When animals are outside, they want to get in. When they're inside, they want to get out. Maybe something's wrong with the tuba."

"It's a squirrel, Doc. I can feel it," said Harry.

"What?"

"Well, the squirrel must have crawled as far as it could into the tuba. If you feel the metal from the bell up, suddenly there's a warm spot where the squirrel must be stuck."

I could picture the tuba in my mind. A tuba is made of ten or fifteen feet of metal tubing. The tubing winds round and round from bell to mouthpiece. Somewhere in that jungle of metal was a poor, confused squirrel. The squirrel must have been too large to move forward and too afraid to move backward.

"Better bring them in," I told Harry. "I don't know what we'll do, but we'll try."

Harry must have made record time coming in from town. He was at the door within twenty minutes. The tuba hung around his neck. Behind him walked a small

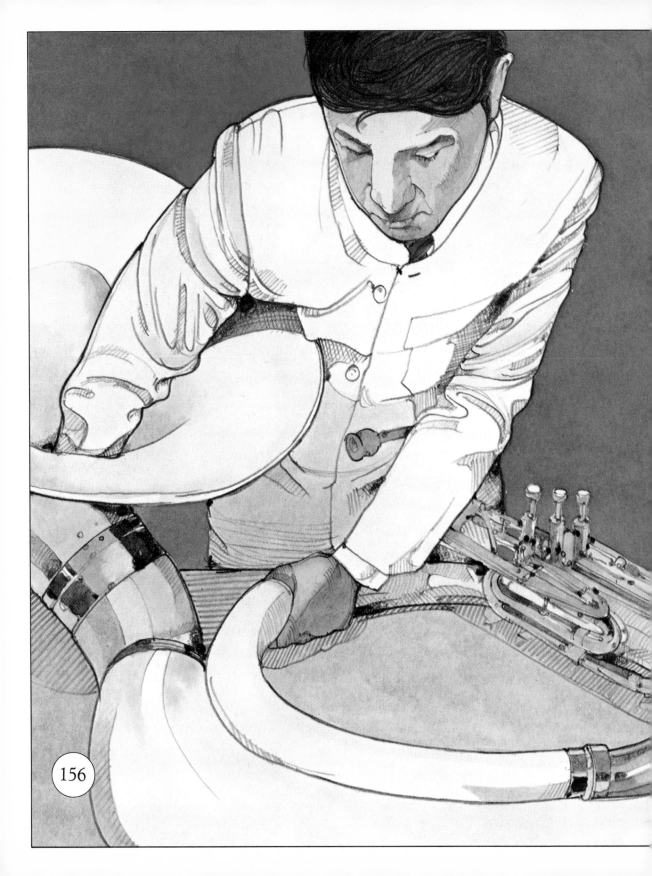

army. There was Jan the tuba player, ruddy-faced and frightened. Jan's mother and father followed her, glancing nervously at their watches. Two or three friends came along to see what would happen.

Harry and Jan moved my hand over the horn until we found the warm spot. There was no doubt about it. There was a living creature inside the horn.

I got to work. I shook the instrument, blew it, and reached into it with small bits of wire. Nothing seemed to work. By now Jan's parents had removed the valves and mouthpiece. We tried pushing wires through the openings. Still no result. I tried putting the mouthpiece on and blowing a few sour, muffled notes. The squirrel did not budge. I tried playing the scale. Some note, I thought, might be just the proper one to excite the squirrel to reverse its tracks.

Meanwhile, the office had become full of interested spectators. News of the problem reached the ears of others in the building. Soon the room was crowded with people who wanted to give advice and watch the operation.

Jan stood by nervously. She moved from one side of me to the other. By now her friends were shifting from foot to foot, glancing at the clock every minute. Suddenly an idea came to me. Chloroform has a strong odor. A little chloroform blown gently into the squirrel's face might make it come out.

I quickly placed a few drops in the mouthpiece, and

157

blew softly into the coil. The room was silent as everyone listened. Were there movements, scratching sounds? I shook the tuba again. Nothing.

As I puffed more chloroform into the mouthpiece, there was a definite sound of scratching. Another shake, and out came a small brown squirrrel. The squirrel was slightly woozy from the chloroform, but kicking spunkily just the same.

A cheer went up from the crowd. Harry clapped me on the back. Jan scooped up her pet and hugged it to her with a smile glowing with happiness. She seemed to light the room. "Thanks, Doc," she mumbled. Then, glancing at the clock, she put the squirrel under one arm, grabbed the tuba, and headed for the door.

The last I saw of Jan was in the big parade. She was marching with the band. Harry and I stood at the curb and cheered as Jan passed. We caught the grateful look and the quick wink she sent our way. She looked great in her uniform, which was all red and gold and . . . brown? We did a double take at Jan's friend, the squirrel we saw peeping from her pocket.

Focus

1. Why did the family call a veterinarian?
2. How did the problem happen?
3. How did Dr. Young finally solve the problem?
4. At the end of the story, how can you tell what Jan felt about her pet?

Coaxing a squirrel out of a tuba took a lot of imagination. In this story a child has imagination and courage, too.

A Thousand Pails of Water

RONALD ROY

Yukio lived in a village where people fished to make their living.

One day Yukio went to the sea to play. Small creatures scurried from under his feet in the tide pools. Large scavenger birds screamed at him from the sky, "Bring us food!"

Then Yukio saw a whale that had become lodged between some rocks and was left behind when the tide went out. The large tail flukes beat the sand, helplessly. The eye, as big as Yukio's hand, rolled in fright. Yukio knew that the whale would not live long out of the sea.

"I will help you, sir," he said.

But how? The whale was huge, like a temple. Yukio raced to the water's edge. Was the tide coming in or

going out? In, he decided, by the way the little fingers of foam climbed higher with each new wave. He knew that if he could keep the whale wet for a while, the tide would soon come in and help the whale swim away.

The sun was hot on Yukio's back as he stood looking at the whale. Suddenly Yukio filled his pail with water and threw it over the great head.

"You are so big and my pail is so small!" he cried. "But I will throw a thousand pails of water over you before I stop."

The second pail went on the head as well, and the third and fourth. But Yukio knew he must wet every part of the whale or it would die in the sun.

Yukio made many trips to the sea for water,

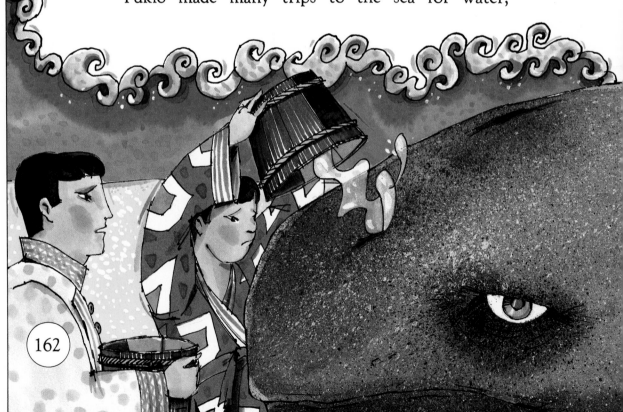

counting as he went. He threw four pails on the body, then four on the tail, and then three on the head. There was a little shade on one side of the big gray prisoner. Yukio sat there, out of breath, his heart pounding. Then he looked in the whale's eye and remembered his promise. Yukio went back to the sea and stooped to fill his pail. How many had he filled so far? He had lost count. But he knew he must not stop.

Then Yukio fell, the precious water spilling from his pail. He cried, and his tears disappeared into the sand. A wave touched his foot, as if to say, "Get up and carry more water. I am coming, but I am very slow."

Yukio filled his pail over and over. His back hurt,

and his arms—but he threw and threw. He fell again, but this time he did not get up. Then Yukio felt himself being lifted.

"You have worked hard, little one. Now let us help."

Yukio's grandfather laid him in the shade of one of the rocks. Yukio watched his grandfather throw his first pail of water and go for another.

"Hurry!" Yukio wanted to scream, for his grandfather was old and walked slowly. Then Yukio heard the voices. His father and the village people were running toward the sea. They carried pails and buckets and anything that would hold water. Some of the villagers removed their jackets and soaked them in the sea.

These they placed on the whale's burning skin. Soon the whale was wet all over.

Slowly the sea came closer and closer. At last it covered the huge tail. The village people ran back and forth carrying water, shouting to each other. Yukio knew the whale would be saved.

Yukio's father came and stood by him. "Thank you, Father," Yukio said, "for bringing the village people to help."

"You are strong and good," his father said. "But to save a whale, many hands must carry the water."

Now the whale was moving with each new wave. Suddenly a great one lifted him free of the rocks. He was still for a moment, then, with a flip of his tail, swam out to sea. The villagers watched silently, as the whale swam farther and farther from their shore. Then they turned and walked toward the village—except for Yukio, who was asleep in the arms of his father. He had carried a thousand pails of water, and he was tired.

Focus

1. What happened to the whale that endangered its life?
2. Why did Yukio keep the whale's body wet?
3. How was the whale saved?
4. What did Yukio learn about needing help to do big jobs?
5. How was Yukio like Roberta in "The Visitor"?

SCIENCE READING: What's It All About?

Do whales and squirrels have anything in common? If they do it isn't size. Both are mammals and both breathe air. You can learn more in your science book about how whales and squirrels are alike.

The next page is like a page in your science book. The subject of the page is "Mammals."

TAKE A FIRST LOOK

Look at the pictures on the page. Ask yourself how the pictures give clues to the information on the page.

FIND KEY IDEAS

Now glance quickly down the page. You will notice several headings. They tell you what each section is about.

Do you see the words in dark type? They are words that may be unfamiliar to you. You can find their meanings in the margin at the left. Sometimes a special spelling follows these words. The special spelling tells you how to pronounce the words.

READ CAREFULLY

Now read the whole page carefully. When you come to a new heading, stop and try to remember the information you have just finished reading.

Be sure you know the meanings of the words in dark type. Pronounce them softly to yourself.

To get all the facts and ideas, you may need to read the page more than once.

MAMMALS

How are elephants, bats, whales, monkeys, squirrels, and rabbits alike? These animals are all part of a group called mammals.

Mammals have hair.

All mammals have hair on their bodies. Some mammals have hair all over their bodies while others have hardly any hair at all. Whales, for example, have just a few whiskers around the mouth.

Mammals have bones.

Run your hand down your arm or leg. Can you feel the bones? If you have a dog or a cat, you can feel its bones, too. All mammals have bones. The bones of an animal make up the animal's **skeleton** (skel'ə tən).

skeleton: all the bones of an animal's body

Mammals breathe air.

Animals need **oxygen** (ok' sə jən) to stay alive. Oxygen is a gas in the air. Mammals have lungs that take oxygen out of the air.

oxygen: a gas in the air that animals breathe

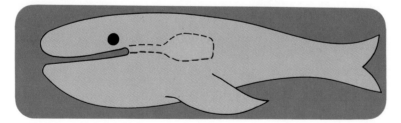

Mammals that live in the sea must come to the surface of the water to breathe air. They cannot take oxygen from the water as fish do. Fish have gills to do this. Whales, otters, and other sea mammals do not have gills. They have lungs. Sea mammals would drown if they could not breathe air.

167

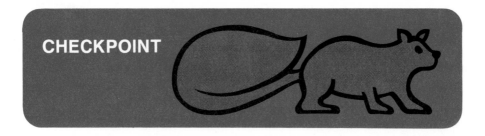

CHECKPOINT

Vocabulary:
Word
Identification

Below are some new words you have learned. Check to see if you know their meanings. First write the vocabulary words on your paper. Then next to each word write the correct definition.

Vocabulary Words
1. muffled
2. staff
3. spectators
4. creature
5. confirm
6. precious

Definitions
show to be true
very valuable
group of workers
people who watch
softened sound
animal or person

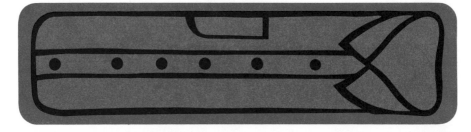

Vocabulary:
Vocabulary
Development
(homophones)

Some words sound the same but have different meanings and are spelled differently. These words are called homophones. On your paper write the word that completes each of the following sentences.

7. The owner of the store decided to have a _____ on shirts.
   sail   sale
8. The rain came _____ a crack in the roof of our treehouse.
   threw   through

168

9. The art teacher gave each child a _____ of drawing paper.
   piece   peace

10. For her birthday Lynnette got some new _____ and a basket-ball.
   close   clothes

Read the paragraph about veterinarians. Decide what the main idea of the paragraph is. Write on your paper the sentence below that tells the main idea of the paragraph.

Comprehension: Main Idea

Veterinarians help animals in many ways. In the story "Squirrel In a What?" you read about a veterinarian who saved a squirrel that was caught in a tuba. In "Animals Need Doctors, Too" you read about veterinarians that take care of farm animals, zoo animals, and pets. Veterinarians take care of sick animals and check up on healthy ones, too. Vets take temperatures and give shots just as your doctor does for you. Have you ever been to a veterinarian's office?

11. Vets
   A veterinarian saved a squirrel that was caught in a tuba.
   Veterinarians do operations on animals that need them.
   Veterinarians help all kinds of animals in different ways.
   Veterinarians take care of healthy animals, too.

169

The Magic

Imagination can take people to places they might otherwise never see. It can make sad times happy. It can make a dull day sparkle. The magic eye of imagination is a wonderful gift.

Imagination can help explain things. How did people discover fire? How are mountains formed?

Imagination can help solve mysteries. In one story a boy detective relies on his imagination to search for a missing person. In another, Jenny Marsh uses her imagination to try to solve a perplexing mystery.

In short, imagination can be used in more ways than most people even think about. This next group of stories will show how.

Eye

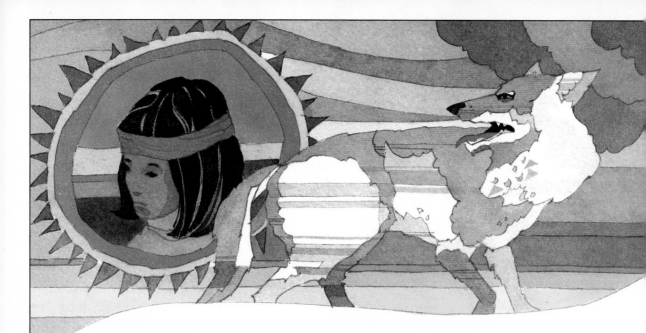

Legends often explain discoveries. This Native American legend explains a discovery of long ago.

The Fire Bringer

MARGARET HODGES

When I hear the old men
Telling of heroes,
Telling of great deeds
Of ancient days,
When I hear them telling,
Then I think within me
I, too, am one of these. . . .

—"A Song of Greatness," translated from the Chippewa
Indian by Mary Austin

The Fire Bringer was an Indian boy. The skin of his body was dark and shining, and he had straight black hair, cut at his shoulders. He wore deerskin belted with a bit of bark, and he ran free on mesa and mountain. He carried in his hand a hunting club made of a cleft stick and a rounded stone. He lived in the long-ago time before fire was brought to the tribes.

The Coyote, the keen gray dog of the wilderness, was the Friend and Counselor of man, and when the boy went out to hunt, the Coyote ran by his side.

In the summer they saw men catching fish in the creeks with their hands. They saw women digging with sharp stones for roots to eat. In the summer they did well.

But when winter came, the people ran shivering in the snow or huddled in caves. The boy saw that they were miserable, and he felt very unhappy.

"My people suffer and have no way to escape the cold," he said.

"I do not feel the cold," said the Coyote.

"That is because you have a fur coat," said the boy. "My people have no fur coats."

"Let them run about, then," said the Coyote. "That will keep them warm."

"They run till they are weary," the boy said, "and there are young children, and old people who cannot run. Help us, O Counselor!"

"There is a way to get help," said the Coyote. "It is very hard, but you and I will take that way together. We must go to the west and bring fire from the Burning Mountain. The tribe must help, too. We will need a hundred men and women, strong and swift runners."

Then he told the boy what fire was, and the boy tried to understand.

"I will find the runners," said the boy. But that was easier to say than to do. Some of the people were lazy and many were afraid. Most of them did not believe the boy could help them, for they said, "We have never heard of fire. How can this boy know something that we do not know?"

But the boy talked much about fire and the people were miserable in the cold. So at last they decided to do what the boy told them. A hundred men and women, the best and fastest runners, said they would go with him.

The Coyote advised them how the march should begin. He and the boy led the way. Next to them went the swiftest runners of the tribe. The others followed according to their strength and speed. They left the place of their home and went over high mountains where great jagged peaks stood up above the snow. They went down the other side of those mountains into a dark woods. The sound of the wind in the branches made them afraid. Here the Coyote stopped.

"Do not fear," he said to the people. "Take your rest."

In the morning he chose one runner to stay in that place, saying, "Wait here until the fire comes."

"How will I know when I see it?" asked the runner. "How does fire look?"

"It is red, like a flower," said the Coyote, "but it is not a flower. You will know it when you see it." He led the tribe on toward the west.

The next night another runner stayed where he was. Again the Coyote led the tribe westward. So it was, at the end of each day's journey, until they came to a great plain where the earth was dry and cracked. The Coyote chose a runner to stay in that place.

"Rest here until the fire comes," he said. "But do not let it touch the grass. Fire can run raging through the grass and devour all before it."

"Is it a beast?" asked the man.

"No, it is not a beast," said the Coyote. "You will know it when you see it."

So they went on until only one runner was left with the boy and the Coyote. Soon they came to another range of hills.

"Stay here," said the Coyote, "until the fire comes." But the last runner asked, "Will the fire come upon me like an enemy?"

"It can be an enemy," the Coyote told him. "It is very fierce and hurtful. Yet, if it is kept among stones and fed with small sticks, it will serve the people well and keep them warm."

Then the Coyote went on with the boy. At the end of the hundred days they came to the Big Water at the foot of the Burning Mountain. The mountain stood up in a high and peaked cone, and the smoke of its burning rolled out and broke along the sky. By night the glare of the fire reddened the waves of the Big Water when the Fire Spirits began their dance.

"There is the fire," said the Coyote. "It has its den inside the mountain, and the Fire Spirits guard it night and day. Stay here until I bring you a brand from the burning. Be ready for running, and lose no time. I shall

be tired when I come again, and the Fire Spirits will chase me."

Then he went up the mountain, and the Fire Spirits laughed when they saw him coming. He was thin, and his coat was much the worse for his long journey. Slinking, shabby, and mean he looked, as he has always looked. He looked like an animal of no importance, so the Fire Spirits paid him no heed.

Along in the night the Fire Spirits began to dance. The Coyote stole a blazing piece of wood and ran with it down the slope of the Burning Mountain.

When the Fire Spirits saw what he had done, they streamed out after him, red and angry, with a sound like a swarm of bees.

The boy saw the Coyote coming with the Fire Spirits after him. He saw the hot sparks stream back along the Coyote's sides as he carried the firebrand in his mouth.

Then the boy stood up in his place, trim and taut for running. He heard the singing sound of the Fire Spirits behind the Coyote.

The boy stood bent for the running as a bow bends to speed the arrow. The good beast panted down beside him and the firebrand dropped from his jaws. The boy caught it up. Out he shot on the homeward path, and the Fire Spirits snapped and sang behind him. As fast as they chased him, he fled faster. Then he saw the next runner stand up in his place to take the firebrand from him.

So the brand passed from hand to hand until they came to the mountains of the snows. These the Fire Spirits could not pass.

The dark, sleek runners with the backward-streaming brand carried it forward until they came in safety to their own land.

Here they kept the fire among stones and fed it with small sticks as the Coyote advised. It warmed them and cooked their food.

As for the boy, he was called the Fire Bringer while he lived. And after that, the Coyote was called the Fire Bringer, since there was no other with so much right to the name.

And this is the sign that the tale is true. All along the Coyote's thin sides the fur is singed and yellow to this very day. This marking was from the flames that blew backward from the brand when the Coyote brought it down from the Burning Mountain.

Focus
1. Why did the Paiute boy want to get fire for his people?
2. Who told him where to get fire?
3. How did the people bring the fire to their home?
4. What do you think "Burning Mountain" means?
5. How did the people use the fire?
6. How did the Coyote get its coloring?

179

The Paiute legend says that fire was kept in a burning mountain. What is a "burning mountain"? Why does it burn?

MOUNTAINS FROM BENEATH THE EARTH

JOHN F. WARNER

Many stories of long ago tell us where fire came from. The Paiute tale explains that a young Indian boy learned about fire from Coyote, the Counselor of Man. Together they went to a burning mountain to bring fire back to the people.

You may have heard other stories of how fire came to people. An early Greek tale explains that a god

named Prometheus brought the gift of fire to people. In this tale Prometheus took fire from a mountain named Olympus.

As in "The Fire Bringer," many of the old tales about fire tell about a burning mountain. The burning mountain of those tales is a volcano.

Where does the word *volcano* come from? It, too, is from an early tale—this time, a Roman one. The Romans of thousands of years ago believed that a god named Vulcan lived deep in the earth. There he kept hot fires burning. Every time Vulcan became angry— which was often, because he had a very bad temper—he would split the earth. Then fire and hot ashes would pour out onto the land. Vulcan's name was used to form the word *volcano.*

Some volcanoes are old, so they have not erupted for years. They are known as extinct or inactive volcanoes. Mount Fuji in Japan is one such volcano. Other volcanoes still burn and erupt fire and hot ashes. They are known as active volcanoes. Mount Kilauea in the Hawaiian Islands is an active volcano. It has erupted more than thirty times in the last twenty-five years! Mount St. Helens, located in Washington State, is another active volcano. On Tuesday, March 27, 1980, Mount St. Helens erupted, shooting smoke, steam, and volcanic ash high into the air.

Volcanoes start deep inside the earth. Vulcan may not be there, but high temperatures are. Sometimes it is so hot there that rocks melt. Gases inside the rocks turn to steam. Then the gases push against the surface of the earth—much the way steam does in a covered pot of boiling water. When the water boils, the steam can become so strong that it pops the lid off the pot.

When the steam inside the earth gets strong enough, it rips a hole in the earth. Out comes the melted rock, called lava. Lava may flow out slowly, like a river of fire. At other times it can blast out with a terrible force.

More than a hundred years ago a volcano destroyed a small island in the Pacific Ocean. The volcano was on the island. Some people say that the eruption of the volcano made the loudest noise ever heard on earth. People many miles away heard the noise. The dust from the eruption rose thousands of feet into the air. After the dust had settled, the island was gone! All that was left was a hole deep in the floor of the ocean.

Many volcanoes are islands in the oceans. Some are hundreds or thousands of years old, and some are quite new. A volcanic island was formed fewer than forty years ago, in Paracutin, Mexico.

In Paracutin a farmer was plowing his cornfield. The field had a low spot, where corn never grew well. But the farmer, Dionisio Polido,* decided that he would try once more to grow corn on that spot. Perhaps this year the corn that he planted would grow. Something did grow—but not corn!

183

*dē ō nēsē ō   pō lē Ho

As Dionisio began planting seeds, he noticed how warm to his touch the earth was. Then he saw smoke rising from the earth. He thought that what he saw was impossible. As he stooped to get a closer look, his hat fell off his head. Just then a low rumble started. The ground began to shake under his feet. Suddenly there was a great roar and the earth split. Rocks blew out of the hole, sending Dionisio's hat flying. He ran away in terror.

A few hours later he returned. A pile of rock as high as a full-grown tree covered the spot where Dionisio had tried to plant corn. Within a week the pile rose to be five hundred feet high. Then lava began to flow out over the pile of rocks. Within two years the lava flow was 1500 feet high. What is more, most of the

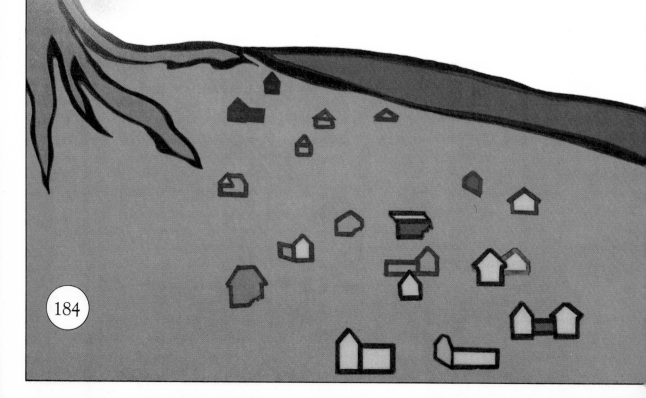

184

village of Paracutin had been buried. Dionisio had seen the birth of a volcano!

No one is sure what makes rocks deep in the earth hot enough to explode and cause volcanoes. Most volcanoes in the world are near each other. If you look at a map of all the volcanoes in the world, you will see a ring of them around the Pacific Ocean. That ring is called the Pacific Ring of Fire.

The country of Japan is part of the ring. There are 33 active volcanoes in Japan. Japan has what many people say is the most beautiful volcano of all. Snow-capped Mount Fuji rises more than 12,000 feet above the sea. It is shaped like a perfect cone and can be seen for miles around. Fuji is Japan's best known landmark.

Fuji is an extinct volcano. It last erupted nearly three hundred years ago. When it did, people in Tokyo, seventy-five miles away, awoke to find the city covered with six inches of volcanic ash. The sky above was dark for many days.

Today Mount Fuji is a famous resort. Every summer people climb its trails to the top. For a time, the

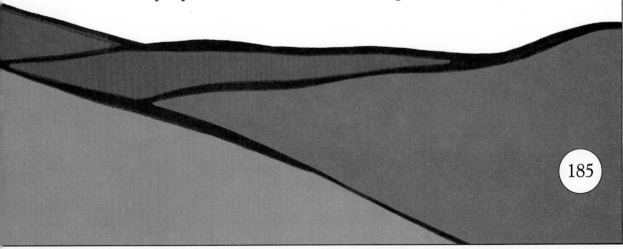

crowds on the mountain were so thick that people had trouble walking. Then a few years ago a cable car was installed. Now, if they want to, people can ride a cable car right to the top of the volcano.

Years ago volcanoes would erupt without warning. In those days whole cities might be destroyed by the burning lava. But now scientists have learned how to tell when a volcano will erupt. If it is to be a big eruption, the people can leave the area.

All volcanic eruptions are not bad. The lava that a volcano leaves becomes rich farming soil. As the people of Japan say, "We don't complain. After all, we have the volcanoes to thank for the ground beneath our feet."

Focus
1. Where does the word *volcano* come from?
2. How does a volcano start?
3. Describe what the farmer saw.
4. Why is Mount Fuji special? Give two or three reasons.
5. Why are some volcanic eruptions good?

187

STUDY SKILL: Encyclopedias

Would you like to live in Japan? You know from reading "Mountains from Beneath the Earth" that Japan has many active volcanoes. Before you decide if you would like to live in Japan, you might want to know more about the country.

An encyclopedia is a good place to look for information on almost any topic. Most encyclopedias have more than 20 volumes. In each volume the topics are listed in alphabetical order. Letters and numbers on the spines help you to find the topics.

Here is a picture of an encyclopedia:

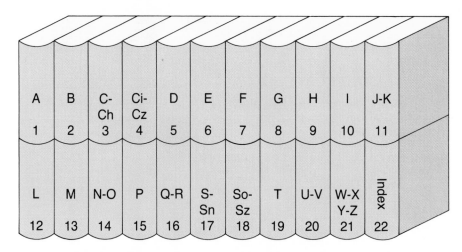

Not all encyclopedias are arranged like the set shown here. Some have more volumes; some have fewer volumes. Some combine letters in different ways.

How can you find information about Japan in an encyclopedia? Look for the volume that has the same letter as the first letter in Japan, the J-K volume. Then use the guide words to help you find the right page.

Most encyclopedia pages have guide words like those on a dictionary page. Look at the top of the page for the guide words. They will help you find the page on which your topic starts.

Suppose you want information about Mount Fuji. You could look for it in the M volume or in the F volume. You may not find the information under M or F. An encyclopedia cannot list every topic. So you may have to look somewhere else. Try the J volume for "Japan." Or try the U-V volume for "volcanoes."

The fastest way of all to find information in an encyclopedia is to use the index. An encyclopedia index lists in alphabetical order all the topics in the set. It will tell you the topic, the volume, and even the page number where you can find the information you want.

Use the picture of the encyclopedia to answer these questions. Write your answers on a sheet of paper.

1. What are guide words in encyclopedias used for?
2. Suppose you were writing a story about fire. In which volume would you look for information on your topic?
3. How would you use an encyclopedia index to help you find information about Mount Kilauea?
4. Suppose you are doing a report on pets. Make a list of topics you could look for in the encyclopedia. Think of topics besides the kinds of pets you will be writing about.
5. Would you expect an encyclopedia to have information on your school? Why or why not? If you wanted to do a report on schools, what topics would you look for in the encyclopedia?

THE WILD GEESE

The wild geese returning
Through the misty sky—
Behold, they look like
A letter written
In faint ink!

TSUMORI KUNIMOTO

The island country of Japan has many volcanoes. It has many legends, too. One of them tells of a poor mountain couple and a wonderful bird.

THE CRANE MAIDEN

MIYOKO MATSUTANI

Long years ago, at the edge of a small mountain village in the snow country of Japan, there lived an old man and his wife. They had little in this world that they could call their own, but they were happy in their life together.

Now one winter morning the old man set out for the village. He had a bundle of firewood fastened to his back. It was bitter cold, and he knew he would have little trouble selling the wood. With the money, he would buy some food so that he and his wife could have a good supper.

As the old man trudged through the falling snow, he was suddenly aware of a fluttering sound. He heard

191

a pitiful cry of *Koh, koh*. Turning from the path to investigate, he came upon a great crane trying to free herself from a trap.

The old man's heart was touched with pity for the magnificent bird. He tried to soothe the crane with tender words while his hands released the cruel spring of the trap. At once the crane flew up, joyfully calling *Koh, koh*, and disappeared into the snowy sky.

With a lighter step the old man went on through the snow. When he had sold his wood he returned once more to his humble house. While his old wife busied herself with preparing supper, he told her about rescuing the crane.

"That was a good deed," she said. "Surely the gods will one day reward you for your kind heart."

As she spoke these words there came a tapping on the door. The old wife hastened to see who was there. Upon opening the door, she saw a beautiful young girl standing in the swirling snow. Her delicate face glowed like a peach beginning to ripen in the summer sun. Her dark eyes sparkled in the firelight from the hearth.

"Forgive my knocking at your door," she said in a soft voice, "but I have lost my way in the snow. May I share the warmth of your fire tonight?"

Then bowing low before the two old people, she said, "My name is Tsuru-san."*

"Oh, you poor child!" cried the old wife. "Come in at once before you freeze in the bitter cold."

They sat the girl down close to the hearth, and the old wife piled more wood on the flames so that the girl would soon be warm. The old couple shared their

*tsü rü sän

simple supper of hot porridge with Tsuru-san, all the time feasting their eyes on her great beauty. Then they gave her their bed with its warm quilts to sleep on. They spent the night huddled on a pile of straw.

In the morning when they awoke, the old man and his wife were surprised to see a good fire already burning on the hearth. The water urn was filled with fresh clear water, the floors had been swept, and all the rooms were clean and tidy.

Tsuru-san, the sleeves of her kimono neatly tied back with a red cord, was busily stirring a pot over the fire. "Good morning," she said, bowing to the old couple. "If you will wash your hands we may eat breakfast, for the porridge is cooked and ready."

"In our old age we have a daughter!" said the old man, laughing.

"It is the gods smiling on us for your good deed of yesterday," replied his wife happily.

The snow and bitter cold continued for many days, and so Tsuru-san stayed in the shelter of the old couple's home. Because she had neither mother nor father, it was at last decided that she would remain as a daughter to these people.

The children of the neighborhood were soon attracted to the house because the girl was such a delight to be with. The house rang with happy laughter, and all hearts were filled with joy at the sound.

And so the days of early winter passed. Soon it would be time for the great New Year celebration. The old man spoke to his wife, saying, "Tsuru-san has been such a delight to us. If only I could give her a gift of a new kimono."

"Or if I could make her a rice cake for the New Year," his wife added.

But the winter had been hard. The old man had not been able to cut much wood to sell. There was no money to buy even rice, much less a kimono.

Now Tsuru-san had overheard them talking, and it grieved her that these good people should be so poor.

Coming before them she bowed low and said, "Dear parents, I know there has been no wood to sell, but perhaps I can help you and repay your great kindness to me. There is an old loom in the back room. I will weave cloth on it for you to sell in the village. Only

you must promise that no one shall look at me while I am weaving."

The old man and his wife thought this was an odd request, but they agreed.

Tsuru-san locked herself in the room. Soon they heard the sound of *Tin kola, kola, pon, pon, Tin kola, kola, pon, pon*—as the shuttle sped back and forth and the fabric grew in length.

For three days this continued. Tsuru-san paused for neither food nor rest. Then at last the door opened and she stepped out. In her hands she held a bolt of cloth such as the old man and his wife had never seen in all their lives. They gasped at its beauty and marveled at its incredible softness.

"Dear father," said the girl, "take this cloth into the village and sell it. It is small payment for the happy home you have given me. Remember this, however," she continued. "Do not put a price on this cloth, and you will fare better than you can imagine."

Without wasting a moment, the old man hurried into the center of the village. When the people saw the beautiful cloth he was carrying, they gathered round to see.

"I will pay ten gold pieces for your cloth," said one man.

"No, no!" cried another. "Sell it to me for twenty gold pieces!"

"You would be a fool to sell it for such a price, old

man," said another. "This is a bolt of rare twilled brocade. I will pay you fifty gold pieces for it."

And so it went, with each man offering more. Finally the old man sold the cloth for a hundred pieces of gold.

He bought only rice for rice cakes, a kimono for Tsuru-san, and a few delicacies for New Year's Day. Then he hurried home with his pockets jingling. "Tomorrow, tomorrow is the New Year's Day," he sang. "The New Year is the happy time. It is the time for eating rice cakes whiter than snow."

Then there was a hustle and bustle as the old man and his wife prepared for the feast. As he pounded the rice, his wife made it into fine cakes. And on New Year's Day all the children came in for a great party with their friend, Tsuru-san.

Still the cold days of winter followed one after the other. At last one day Tsuru-san said to the old couple, "It is time for me to weave another bolt of cloth for you so that you will have money to live until the spring returns. But remember what I told you. No one is to look at me while I am working."

Again they promised that they would not. Then the girl once more locked herself in the room and began weaving.

Tin kola, kola, pon, pon, Tin kola, kola, pon, pon—

went the loom. One day passed, and then the second. Still the sound of the loom filled the house. By now, the neighbors had grown curious.

"Is Tsuru-san weaving again?" asked one.

"Ah, soon you will have more gold pieces to hide under the floor," said another with a smile and a wink.

"The loom makes such an interesting sound," remarked the first one. "I would love to see what Tsuru-san is doing."

"We have promised not to watch her while she works," said the old man.

"What an odd request," cried one of the people.

"I would not make such a promise to my daughter. What harm could there be in taking one look?"

Now, the old woman had been most curious about Tsuru-san's weaving. Encouraged by her neighbor's remarks, she stepped up to a crack in the door.

"Stop, stop!" cried her husband when he saw what was happening. "Tsuru-san has forbidden it!"

But it was too late. His wife had already peeked through the crack.

What a sight it was that met her eye! There, sitting at the loom, was a great white crane, pulling feathers from her body. The crane was weaving the feathers into

a beautiful brocade cloth.

The old woman stepped back from the door. Before she could relate what she had seen, the door opened. Out stepped Tsuru-san, thin and pale, holding in her hands a half-finished bolt of cloth.

"Dear parents," she said in a weak voice, "I am the crane you rescued from the trap. I wanted to repay your kindness by weaving you another bolt of cloth." Then her eyes filled with tears. "But now that you have seen me in my true form, I can no longer stay with you."

With this she kissed the man and his wife tenderly and walked out of the house. Instantly she became a crane once more, and with a great whish of her wings flew up into the sky. Slowly she circled overhead. Then, with a single cry of *Koh* as if to say good-by, the crane maiden was gone forever.

Focus

1. What did the old man discover in the woods?
2. Why did Tsuru-san come to live with the old people?
3. Tsuru-san wanted to repay the old couple for being kind parents to her. How did she repay them for their kindness?
4. What did Tsuru-san ask the couple to avoid doing?
5. Why did Tsuru-san turn back to a crane?

Vocabulary:
Word
Identification

Use the following words to complete the sentences below. Write the completed sentences on your paper.

explode   temperature   journey
swift   devour   keen

1. The coyote said that raging fire could _____ the grass.
2. An erupting volcano shoots out lava whose _____ can be 2000 degrees C (3600 degrees F).
3. The Fire Bringer needed _____ runners to help him bring the fire from the Burning Mountain.
4. A volcano can _____ with great force.

Vocabulary:
Vocabulary
Development
(multiple meanings)

Each of the following words has more than one meaning. Use each word twice and complete the sentences below. On your paper write the completed sentences.

crane   rose   leaves   spoke   second

5. The wheel on my bicycle has a broken _____.
6. Tsuru-san was not really a girl, she was a _____.
7. I am the _____ person in line.
8. The Paiute boy _____ to the coyote.
9. The crane _____ into the sky.
10. The wind blew the _____ off the tree.
11. A _____ is a big machine.
12. The girl _____ school everyday at 3:00 P.M.
13. A _____ is shorter than a minute.
14. My favorite flower is the _____.

Some statements give you facts. Others give opinions. Write the statements below on your paper. Next to each statement write either the word *fact* or the word *opinion*.

15. The Fire Bringer was a Paiute boy.
16. The coyote helps people more than any other animal.
17. Mount Fuji, in Japan, is the most beautiful volcano in the world.
18. Many volcanoes are islands in the oceans.
19. Tsuru-san wove cloth for her parents to sell.
20. Cranes are more graceful than swans.

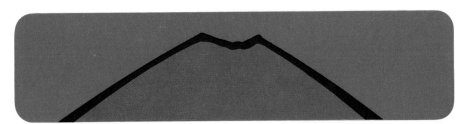

Read the words and sentences below. Complete each sentence with a word from the list. Write the completed sentences on your paper.

advised	fiction	inadvisable	patiently	acted
inactive	impatient	react	nonfiction	patient

21. An _____ volcano is not dangerous.
22. The neighbors were _____ to learn the mystery of Tsuru-san's weaving ability.
23. It was _____ for the people to watch the crane maiden working at the loom.
24. A _____ book usually tells facts about a subject.

203

Imagination and knowledge greatly help in solving mysteries. The famous young detective, Encyclopedia Brown, uses his knowledge and that of Chief Brown, his father, to try to solve a mystery.

Encyclopedia Brown:
The CASE of the WANTED MAN

DONALD J. SOBOL

"I'm never going to shave."

Encyclopedia glanced up from his book. Standing in the door of the Brown Detective Agency was six-year-old Bryan Horton.

"You're never going to shave?" asked Encyclopedia, pretending to be serious. "But you must. Beards aren't allowed in second grade."

"Shaving takes too much time," said Bryan. "When I grow up and get my picture taken, I'll just pull off my beard."

"Ouch!" said Encyclopedia.

Bryan looked surprised. "Does it hurt to pull off your beard?"

"Only around the face," answered Encyclopedia.

"The man didn't hurt himself," said Bryan. "He was smiling."

"What man?" asked Encyclopedia.

"The man who pulled off his beard to have his

picture taken," said Bryan impatiently. "What kind of detective are you?"

Talking with a boy of six wasn't always easy, decided Encyclopedia. He started over. "Do you need help?"

"That's why I'm here, isn't it?" said Bryan. "I want you to read the big words under the man's picture. It's hanging in the post office. Boy, he must be famous."

"Famous?" yelped Encyclopedia. "He's a wanted man. Only dangerous crooks have their pictures hanging in the post office!"

Encyclopedia rolled out his bike. He put Bryan on the crossbar and rode swiftly to the post office.

"After I saw the man pull off his beard, my Mom took me with her to mail a package," said Bryan. "She got sore when I played with the stamp machine. She made me stand over there." He pointed to a bulletin board on the post office wall. A lot of small posters were tacked to one corner.

"That's him," said Bryan. "The one on top."

Encyclopedia saw two photographs of a clean-shaven young man. One showed him full-faced, the other from the side. There were small pictures of each of his ten fingerprints and a line of heavy type: "WANTED FOR ARMED HOLDUP."

Encyclopedia read further: "William Matson, alias Billy, Bill, The Kid." Below this was smaller type giving Matson's long criminal record.

"Wow! This is a case for Dad," exclaimed Encyclopedia. He telephoned his father at once. Then he questioned Bryan.

He learned that Bryan now lived at the Beach Motel, which Bryan's father had just bought. That morning Bryan had seen the wanted man, William Matson, get into his car, pull off his beard, and drive away.

"He wasn't going to have his picture taken," explained Encyclopedia. "This photograph was taken three years ago. See, there's the date. The beard was fake. He wore it so nobody would know him."

When Chief Brown arrived at the post office, Encyclopedia repeated what he had learned.

"Matson must not have seen Bryan," said Chief Brown. "Otherwise, he would not have risked taking off his beard. It probably itched. So he took it off as soon as he could."

"Do you think he'll come back to the motel?" asked Encyclopedia.

"Little chance of that," replied Chief Brown. "But perhaps he left a clue in his room that will tell us where he is going."

Chief Brown returned to the patrol car. Encyclopedia did not see him again till dinner. Chief Brown finished his barley soup before bringing up the case.

"William Matson spent a week at the Beach Motel under the name Bill Martin. He paid his bill and drove to the airport."

207

"How did you find that out, Dad?"

"Bryan's father writes down the license plate numbers of everyone who stops at his motel," said Chief Brown. "Matson's license began with an E, the letter given to all rented cars in the state. We traced the car to the airport branch of Easy Car Rental Service."

"Did Matson get on a plane?" asked Encyclopedia.

"Very likely," said Chief Brown. "But he uses so many different names that he can't be traced as a passenger." Chief Brown took a slip of paper from his pocket before continuing.

"Bryan's father overheard Matson talking on the pay telephone," said Chief Brown. "He didn't hear much except the words, 'ticket to Moscow.' Matson wrote several places on a pad in his room. He forgot that his pencil dug into the sheet beneath. I had the writing brought out." Chief Brown passed the paper to Encyclopedia. On it was written: Moscow, Odessa, London, Paris, Palestine, Athens.

"Matson has been mixed up in jewelry thefts," said Chief Brown. "He must have hidden here in Idaville till he thought it was safe to move his loot. That list must be of places where he hopes to sell the stolen jewels."

Mrs. Brown picked up the piece of paper. She studied it for a long moment.

"It's a strange list," she said. "Two cities in Russia—Moscow and Odessa. Then look here. Lon-

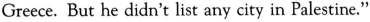

don is in England, Paris is in France, and Athens is in Greece. But he didn't list any city in Palestine."

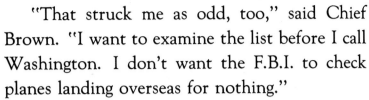

"That struck me as odd, too," said Chief Brown. "I want to examine the list before I call Washington. I don't want the F.B.I. to check planes landing overseas for nothing."

Encyclopedia had closed his eyes. He was doing his deepest thinking.

"Matson didn't fly across the ocean," he said. "You'll find him in—"

WHERE?

Solution to "The Case of the Wanted Man"

Encyclopedia saw what was wrong—the word *Palestine*. Palestine is the old name for Israel. If William Matson were going there, he would have written *Israel*. So Encyclopedia knew the list was not what it seemed at first glance—names of foreign places. He told his father that Matson had flown to Texas. And that is where the police arrested him—in a motel in Palestine, Texas. Encyclopedia remembered that Moscow, Odessa, London, Paris, Athens, and Palestine are names of towns in Texas!

Focus

1. Who is the Wanted Man and why is he wanted?
2. What clues did Chief Brown uncover?
3. What clues did Encyclopedia use to solve the case?

209

The Case of the Wanted Man was like a puzzle. Here are some puzzles for you to try. At first they may seem tricky. But if you think long enough you will probably find the solutions.

Perplexing Puzzles and Tantalizing Teasers

MARTIN GARDNER

How Clever are You?

Are you good at thinking of simple ways to solve difficult problems? Try to solve the following problems.

1. You see a truck that has become stuck beneath an underpass. The truck is an inch too tall to continue passing through. There is a filling station and garage a short distance down the road. The driver of the truck is starting to walk toward the garage to get help. Suddenly a bright idea pops into your head. You tell the driver your idea. Five minutes later he is through the underpass and on his way.
   What did you tell him to do?

2. You are a camper on a hike with your friends. After walking through a small town on your way to

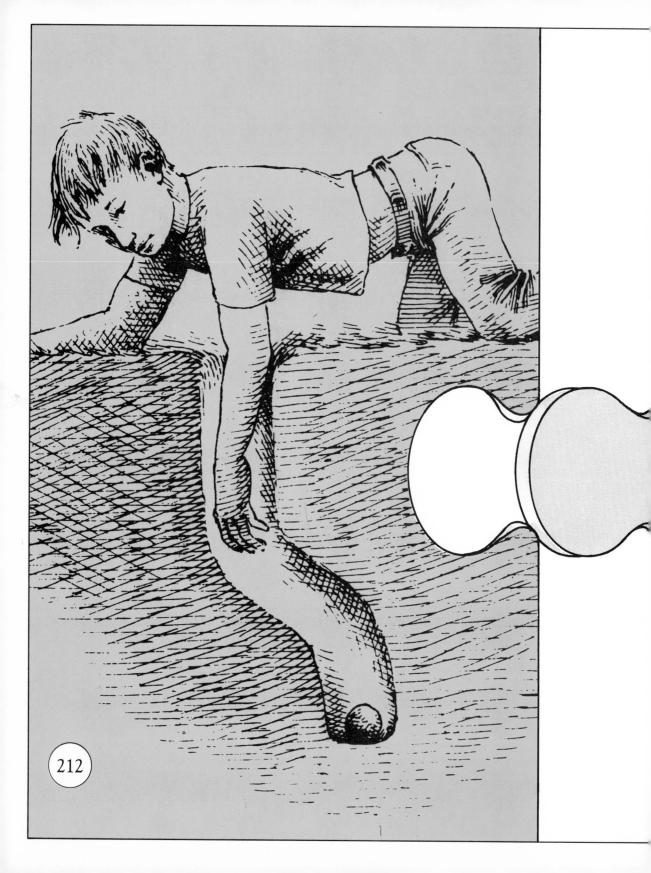

Mudville, you reach a spot where two roads cross. A signpost has been knocked over and is lying on its side. None of you knows which road leads to Mudville. Then you remember something that will solve your problem.

What do you remember?

3. You are playing a game of Ping-Pong in the backyard of a friend's house. When you miss the ball, it bounces across the lawn and rolls into a small but deep hole. The hole goes down too far for you to reach the ball with your hand. The hole also curves so much to one side that you can't get the ball by poking a stick into the hole. After a few minutes you think of an easy way to get the ball.

What did you think of?

Solutions

1. You tell the driver to let some air out of his tires. This lowers the truck enough to let it through the underpass. The driver can stop at the garage ahead and put the air back in his tires.

2. You remember the name of the town you have just left. You place the signpost back in the hole with the name of the town you have left pointing back along the road you have just traveled. All the other signs will have to be pointing in the right directions.

3. You fill the hole with water from a hose and the Ping-Pong ball floats to the top.

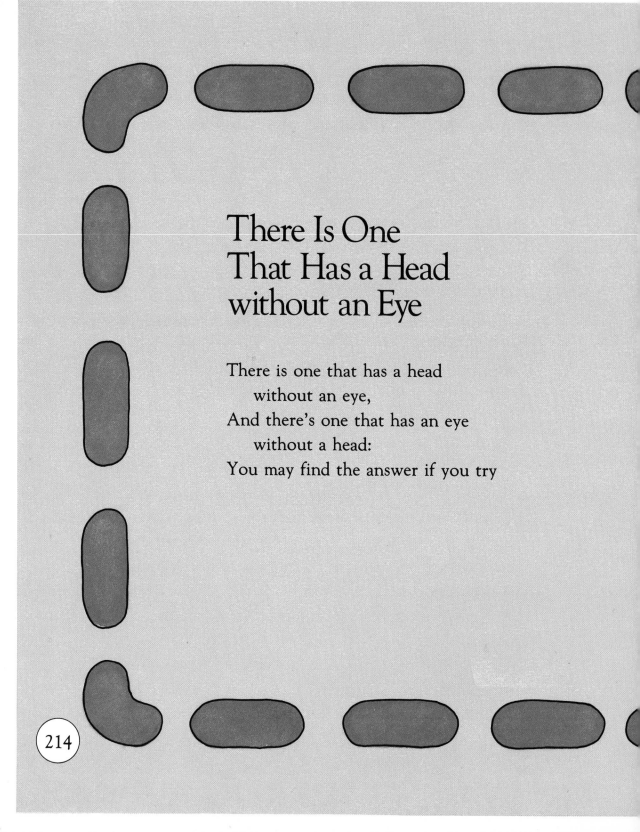

There Is One
That Has a Head
without an Eye

There is one that has a head
    without an eye,
And there's one that has an eye
    without a head:
You may find the answer if you try

And when all is said,
Half the answer hangs upon a thread.

CHRISTINA ROSSETTI

Perplexing puzzles are fun and satisfying to solve. People do them for fun. But Jenny and Carlos face a more serious puzzle.

The Mystery of the Rolltop Desk

EVELYN WITTER

Jenny watched her mother pull the red pickup truck into the driveway. A large canvas-covered object was tied up in the back.

"What do you suppose Mom's bringing home this time?" her brother, Roger, asked.

At that moment Mrs. Marsh breezed through the door, plugged in the coffee pot, and turned to face them. Her face was pale. Her hands trembled.

"What did you buy?" Jenny asked.

"I was helping Mr. Sloan get ready for the auction, as I do every Friday. I saw a rolltop desk. I asked Mr.

Sloan if I could buy it before the Saturday auction and he said 'yes' and so I did. Then a man came in and insisted on buying it. I said 'no' but he kept insisting. Finally, I just left with the desk."

"That shouldn't make you nervous, Mom."

"But he followed me home!"

Now Jenny began to feel nervous. She parted the kitchen curtains and looked out the window. Clouds floated over the blue sky. The sun shone brightly. Everything seemed peaceful. Then Jenny saw a man getting out of a small, green car. He was neatly dressed in navy blue and had a bushy moustache. He was looking at their house.

"I see him!" Jenny exclaimed.

Mrs. Marsh sipped her coffee. "He's odd," she said. "He even grabbed me by the arm when I refused to sell the desk. He kept saying he just had to have that desk."

"What is so special about the desk?" Roger asked.

"Let's unload it. You can see for yourself," Mrs. Marsh suggested.

"I'll get Carlos to help," Jenny said as she hurried out. She was back in a few minutes with Carlos Martinez, the boy who lived next door and who was her best friend.

Roger soon had the ropes untied and the canvas peeled away from the desk. Carlos had his father's moving helper—a platform on a roller that his father called a dolly. The children wheeled the desk up the

stairs and into the living room.

When the desk was in place, Jenny told Carlos about the odd man who said he just had to have it.

"Why does he have to have this particular one?" Carlos asked.

"It's a good desk," Mrs. Marsh said. "And it is an old one."

Jenny studied the desk. It had eight big drawers, twenty pigeonholes, and sixteen little drawers.

"It would hold a lot of stuff," Jenny said.

"Why this desk?" Carlos asked again.

Jenny was about to give her opinion when she noticed the green car again. She grabbed a pencil and began writing.

"What are you writing?" her mother asked.

"His license number," Jenny replied.

That night Jenny helped her mother check all the windows and doors to see that they were locked. But Jenny had a strange feeling. Even though the house was locked up, if anyone really wanted to get in she felt that it wouldn't be hard. She woke several times during the night.

Finally, since she couldn't sleep, she crept downstairs. She walked over to the desk. She lit the light near it. She kept asking herself what there was about the desk that made the man want it so much.

With nimble fingers Jenny touched every drawer and every pigeonhole. As far as she could see, there was nothing unusual about them.

Then Jenny gradually pulled the big desk away from the wall. She looked at the back of the desk. She smoothed her fingers all around the back. The oak boards were smooth. Then she felt one spot where the varnish felt thicker than the rest. Jenny ran her fingers over that spot again. Then she thumped the spot with her fist. It sounded hollow.

She kept tapping the same spot. She could see a square crack beginning to form as she tapped.

Quickly she ran next door. She threw pebbles at Carlos' window to wake him. She wanted to share her discovery with Carlos.

After three throws, Carlos came to his window. "What's the matter?" he asked with a yawn.

"Hurry!" Jenny told him.

A few minutes later Carlos was in the Marshes' living room. As soon as he saw the square crack and thumped the back of the desk himself, he ran to the garage and got a chisel and hammer. The two worked quickly and quietly. Jenny and Carlos soon had the square pried loose.

There, lying in the circle of light from the lamp, was a piece of yellowed paper. It had some old-fashioned writing on it. In places the writing was almost all faded away. There were three ink blots between two of the lines. The writing was hard to read. Jenny and Carlos finally figured it out. It read:

> *"Howe's fleet in Chesapeake Bay.*
> *Plans to sail to Philadelphia.*
> *G. Washington."*

"George Washington!" exclaimed Carlos.

"Written by George Washington!" echoed Jenny. "That's what the man really wants!"

"Keep it locked in your dresser," whispered Carlos. "I'll be back in the morning and we'll tell your mom and dad."

The next morning Jenny was awakened by her mother's call. "Jenny! Roger! Come down!"

Jenny threw on her robe and hurried downstairs. She saw desk drawers piled on the sofa and stacked on the floor. The desk was lying on its side. The hole in the back was plain to see.

Jenny tried to pull her mother aside and tell her about the paper she and Carlos had found, but the police had already arrived.

"May we check this place out?" one officer asked.

While the police checked for fingerprints, Jenny and Roger met Carlos in the garage at the back of the Marsh property.

"Should we tell them about the paper we found?" Carlos asked.

"We should," Jenny said.

"I don't believe the man in the green car was the one who broke in last night," Roger said thoughtfully.

"He would know that Mom could identify him."

"Maybe," said Carlos, "but he looked awfully suspicious yesterday when he parked his car around here."

"Let's go back to the house," Jenny said.

Back in the house they listened carefully to the questions the police asked and watched the shorter officer check for fingerprints. The tall officer explained:

"We're checking these fingerprints against those of two men we caught last night. We're certain that these are the men who ransacked the rolltop desk. We know that these men have been convicted of break-ins in which valuable documents have been taken. If these fingerprints match theirs, then we're certain that a valuable document is involved."

Just then the doorbell rang. When Jenny opened the door, she gasped and took three steps backward. There stood the neatly dressed man.

"I beg your pardon," he said in a low voice. "My name is Darrell Young. May I please speak with Mrs. Marsh?"

"My mother doesn't want to sell her desk," Jenny told him. She tried to be calm, but she knew the quiver in her voice told how frightened she was.

"I know," said the young man. "I must speak to her and explain about the desk."

Jenny hurried into the living room. "Mom! That man is here—that man in the green car—he's at the front door asking for you!"

"Show him in," ordered the tall officer.

The man followed Jenny into the living room. He stopped short when he saw the officer.

"I'm Darrell Young," he stammered. "I seem to have bungled this whole mission."

"What mission?" asked the officer.

"I represent the Farley Museum," said Mr. Young. He drew out papers and gave them to the officer.

"These papers appear to be in order, Mr. Young," said the police officer. "What is your business here?"

"This is my first assignment," explained Mr. Young. "I was to purchase the rolltop desk. The museum traced this desk back to a man who was a Virginian. The Virginian was the owner of a document dating back to the American Revolution. The museum had reason to believe that when the Virginian bought the desk, he transferred all his papers to it."

"The American Revolution document, too?" asked Jenny.

"Yes," nodded Mr. Young. "Well, I tried several times to get Mrs. Marsh to sell the desk, but she just wouldn't."

"Do you have any knowledge of two men who make a specialty of taking documents?" the officer asked.

"I do know of several rare documents that have been taken in burglaries. It's possible that the two men could have known about the Washington document and broken in here and taken it," said Mr. Young.

"No, they didn't!" cried Jenny. "I have it."

All eyes were on Jenny and Carlos as they told how they had found the secret drawer. Jenny ran upstairs and brought the yellowed paper to Mr. Young.

"That's it!" cried Mr. Young, trembling with excitement. "And George Washington's signature is clear. This is indeed a great find!"

Everyone gathered around Mr. Young.

"We'll have to hold those men," said the tall officer. "They didn't get what they were looking for, but these prints will probably prove that they did the breaking and entering."

"The museum will pay you handsomely for this document, Mrs. Marsh," Mr. Young cut in. "And of course, Jenny and Carlos will receive a citation for protecting a valuable historic document."

"They solved the mystery of the rolltop desk before any of us," Mrs. Marsh added proudly.

Jenny and Carlos smiled happily at each other.

Focus

1. At the beginning of the story, what happened that made Mrs. Marsh nervous?
2. What discovery did Jenny and Carlos make?
3. What interest did Mr. Young have in the desk?
4. At the end of the story, how were Jenny and Carlos rewarded?

225

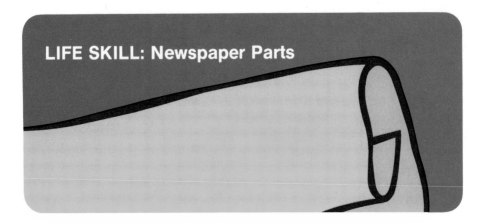

LIFE SKILL: Newspaper Parts

Jenny and Carlos solved the mystery of the rolltop desk. If the story had been true, it might have been printed in their local newspaper like this:

DESK HIDES HISTORIC DOCUMENT
Local Children Solve Mystery

A letter signed by George Washington was found yesterday by Jennifer Marsh. The letter dates back to the American Revolution. It was found in a secret drawer of a rolltop desk. Mrs. Marsh bought the desk yesterday at an auction.

Dr. Darrell Young of the Farley Museum said, "This is a great find. George Washington's signature is quite clear." Jennifer was helped by Carlos Martinez, a friend. Both will get awards for the find.

Stories like this one are news. News stories give facts about important events. If the story of the rolltop desk appeared in a local newspaper, it might be on the front page. That is where the most important news is printed. But in a big-city newspaper the story of the letter might not be front-page news.

Newspapers have feature stories, too. Features can include stories about pets, vacations, and gardens. They may also tell about a school play or a concert.

Sometimes readers send letters to the newspaper. If the letters are printed, they appear in the editorial section of the newspaper. The editorial section is where the newspaper owners and readers give their opinions about items in the news.

Photos and art help to make a newspaper interesting. These appear in every part of a newspaper. So do advertisements. Stores and other businesses pay to have their ads in the newspaper.

Look again at the newspaper story about Jenny and Carlos. What catches your eye? You probably see the title, or headline. Headlines give a summary of the story. The most important stories have the biggest headlines. Most news stories appear in the first section of the paper.

The rest of the paper is organized by subject. Most newspapers have an index to help you find the subjects easily. Suppose you want to see a movie. You could look through the pages of the newspaper until you find the movie section. But a faster way would be to look in the index for the page number of the movie section. The index usually is on the first or second page. It lists the sections in alphabetical order.

Now, on a separate piece of paper, answer the questions below.

1. What kinds of stories would you expect to find on the front page of a big-city newspaper?
2. Why do you think a newspaper is divided into sections? Name at least four sections.
3. Explain the difference between an ad and a news story.
4. What might you find in the editorial section of a newspaper?
5. Why does a newspaper have an index? How is it used?
6. Write headlines for newspaper stories that might be printed about "The Fire Bringer" and "The Crane Maiden."

CHECKPOINT

Vocabulary:
Word
Identification
Below are six new words followed by six questions. Answer each question by using a word from the list. Use each word once.

quiver   solution   citation
purchase   bulletin   license

1. Which word describes the answer to a problem?
2. Which word means "to buy"?
3. What kind of official paper gives permission to do something?
4. Which word means "to shake or tremble"?
5. What is a brief news item called?
6. How might official praise for public service be given?

Comprehension:
Author's
Purpose
Think about the mystery stories you have just read. In those stories do the authors want to teach you something, to tell a good story, or to try to convince you to do something? Read the following paragraph. What is the main purpose of this paragraph? Write your answer on your paper.

228

Bicycles with flat tires are of no use. However, you can learn to fix flats yourself. First remove the wheel. Then take the tire off the rim. Remove the inner tube. Find the hole in the inner tube and seal it with a patch. Replace the tube and the tire. Then replace the wheel and inflate the tire. There, you've fixed the flat!

7. The main purpose of this paragraph is:
   a. to tell you a story
   b. to tell you how to do something
   c. to make you want to do something

Below are the names of sections or parts of a newspaper. Use the list to help you answer the following questions. Write the answers on your paper.

Life Skill:
Resources
(newspaper parts)

comics   entertainment   weather
news   ads   sports

8. In which section of the newspaper would you look if you wanted to buy a used bike?
9. In which section of the newspaper could you read about the hockey playoffs?
10. Where in the newspaper would you look to find out what movies are playing?
11. In which part of the newspaper could you find out yesterday's high and low temperatures?
12. In which section of the newspaper would you look to find out about the president's speech?

Harness the

W

Discoveries are exciting. Just think back to some of the discoveries you have made. Some discoveries are made only once. Others are made everyday by thousands of people. Each discovery is important to the one who made it.

One kind of discovery can lead to finding out about yourself. Then there is the kind of discovery that leads nature to help us, like Windwagon Jones's idea to harness the wind.

Now there are more discoveries to be made. They lie in wait on the pages of this unit.

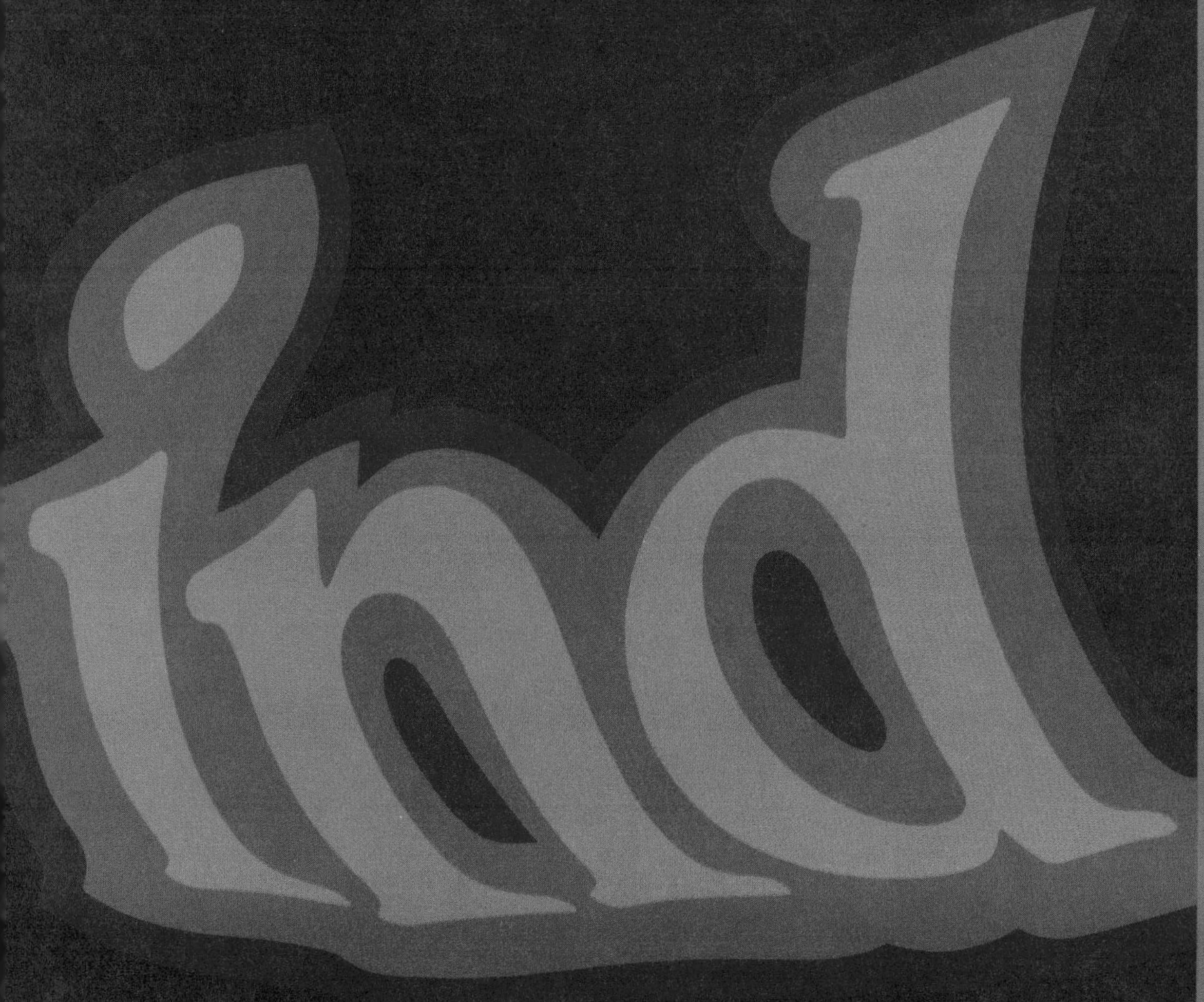
ind

The telephone brings people together even though they may be miles apart. But the telephone can be of help in an emergency, too.

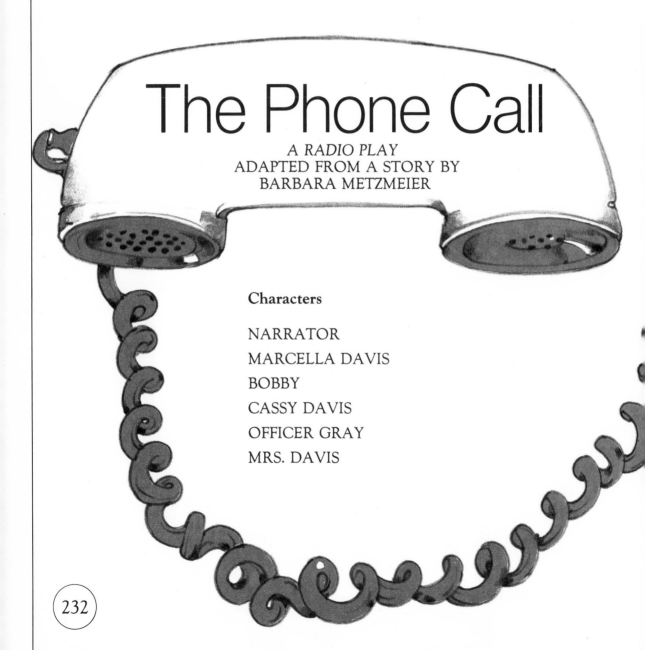

The Phone Call

A RADIO PLAY
ADAPTED FROM A STORY BY
BARBARA METZMEIER

Characters

NARRATOR

MARCELLA DAVIS

BOBBY

CASSY DAVIS

OFFICER GRAY

MRS. DAVIS

NARRATOR: Marcella Davis lay on the sofa watching the rain. She had to stay home and take care of her sister while her mother was out, and she was bored. She'd just finished reading her last library book, her sister Cassy was sleeping upstairs, and there was nothing on television that she felt like watching. *(thunder)* She was on her way into the kitchen to fix a snack when the phone rang. *(telephone rings)*

MARCELLA: Hello?

BOBBY: *(frightened)* Mama's sick!

MARCELLA: What? Who is this?

BOBBY: Mama's sick!

MARCELLA: What's wrong with her? Where is she?

BOBBY: She's on the floor.

MARCELLA: Where are you? Who is this? *(pause)* Are you still there? Please, don't hang up. What's your name?

BOBBY: *(shouts)* Bobby!

NARRATOR: There was a bang, and Marcella knew Bobby had dropped the phone.

MARCELLA: Bobby, come back!

NARRATOR: But Marcella knew it was too late. She didn't know what to do. She could run across the street and get Mrs. Robbins, but in the meantime Bobby might come back and hang up the phone. A flash of lightning filled the window. *(loud thunder)*

BOBBY: Mama's sick.

MARCELLA: You're back! *(trying to sound cheerful)* Hi, Bobby, my name is Marcella.

233

BOBBY:	Mar-cell-ah.
MARCELLA:	Yes, that's right, that's good. Now, listen Bobby . . . are you listening?
BOBBY:	Uh-huh.
MARCELLA:	Where do you live?
BOBBY:	I live in a big house.
MARCELLA:	Good. Do you know your street, Bobby? Do you know its name?
BOBBY:	My street? No. My name is Bobby! I told you!
NARRATOR:	Marcella rubbed her forehead. Her own mother had made her and Cassy memorize their address and phone number as soon as they were old enough to memorize. She wished that Bobby knew his street and phone number.
MARCELLA:	Bobby, what color is your house?
BOBBY:	Purple. *(giggle)*
MARCELLA:	Purple? You're teasing, Bobby. What color is the outside wall?
BOBBY:	Green.
MARCELLA:	The outside of your house—is it red brick? White wood? Stone? Close your eyes and remember what your house looks like.
NARRATOR:	The phone banged down again. Marcella was getting worried. She didn't know what was wrong with Bobby's mother, but she probably needed help quickly. They couldn't keep wasting time like this.
BOBBY:	*(out of breath)* It's . . . it's brick and it's all . . . all wet outside from the rain.

234

235

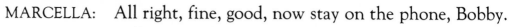

MARCELLA: All right, fine, good, now stay on the phone, Bobby. Tell me, can you read?

BOBBY: *(sadly)* No.

MARCELLA: Do you know your ABC's?

BOBBY: Sure, abcdefg hijk lmnop qrstuv wxyz!

MARCELLA: That's great, that's really good. Do you remember what the letters look like?

BOBBY: Sure.

MARCELLA: All right, now where are you? What room are you in?

BOBBY: The kitchen.

MARCELLA: Fine, good. Now listen, Bobby, we're going to play a game. Look around until you see something with letters on it—but don't leave the phone!

BOBBY: The cereal box has letters on it.

MARCELLA: Good. Now, don't leave the phone, but tell me what the letters are.

BOBBY: c . . . o . . . r . . . n . . . f . . . l . . . a . . . k . . . e . . . s.

MARCELLA: Very good, just right, Bobby. Do you want to play another game?

BOBBY: Yes, but Mama's sick!

MARCELLA: I know, and we're going to help her, but first let's play this game. It's reading numbers. You know how to read numbers, don't you?

BOBBY: 1, 2, 3, 4. . . .

MARCELLA: *(interrupting)* Fine, good. Now, look at the telephone. Do you see, right in the center of the round

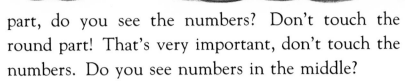

part, do you see the numbers? Don't touch the round part! That's very important, don't touch the numbers. Do you see numbers in the middle?

BOBBY: Uh-huh, there are numbers in the middle, and then numbers all around it.

MARCELLA: That's right, that's good. Now listen very carefully. The game is to read those numbers in the middle. Can you read them to me?

BOBBY: Sure. There's a 5 and a 5 and a 5, and then something, a little line, and then 0 . . . 6 . . . 9 . . . 8.

MARCELLA: Oh, Bobby, that's wonderful!

NARRATOR: Marcella's hand shook with excitement as she wrote down the number. Now she had something to tell the police.

BOBBY: Do I win?

MARCELLA: You sure do! Now just stay on the phone. I'm going to get my little sister. I know she'd like to talk to you. I think she's just about your age. How old are you, Bobby?

BOBBY: I'm three and a half.

MARCELLA: Well, my sister is seven. Now hang on. Don't hang up.

NARRATOR: Marcella ran to the bedroom and woke up Cassy in a hurry.

MARCELLA: Wake up, wake up, Cassy! There's somebody on the phone, a little boy, and he wants to talk to you.

CASSY: To me? On the telephone?

MARCELLA: Come on, hurry up. (*running*) Okay, now, here, his name is Bobby. You talk to him. This is very important: don't let him hang up. Talk to him until I get back. I have something to tell him.

CASSY: Hello? Bobby? My name is Cassy. Is it raining where you are?

NARRATOR: Marcella rushed out into the rain. She didn't stop for an umbrella or coat. She was soaked right away. Her shoes slushed as they filled with water. The thunder roared, but now it didn't frighten her. She banged on Mrs. Robbins' door and told the elderly lady what had happened. She asked her to call the police, and gave her the telephone number. Then she ran back to her own house. Cassy had run out of things to say on the telephone, but Bobby was still there. Marcella got a storybook and read to Bobby.

BOBBY: That was a pretty good story. (*yawns*) Read me another story.

MARCELLA: All right, I will, but don't fall asleep, Bobby.

BOBBY: Okay—wait. The doorbell is ringing.

NARRATOR: The phone dropped again. After a moment, Marcella could hear voices in the background. She waited for what seemed like a long time, trying to sort out the noises she could hear.

OFFICER GRAY: Hello? Is this Marcella Davis? This is Officer Gray.

MARCELLA: Yes, this is Marcella Davis. Is everything all right?

OFFICER GRAY: Yes, I think so. Bobby's mother fell on the stairs, and she may have fainted. But she's awake now. Her ankle has been hurt. We have a doctor here, and he thinks everything is going to be fine, thanks to you. You're the one who should be thanked. That was quite a detective job you did, young lady!

MARCELLA: I didn't know what to do at first. How's Bobby?

OFFICER GRAY: (laughs) He crawled onto the sofa and fell asleep.

MARCELLA: Listen, I'd better hang up. I just heard my mother come in.

OFFICER GRAY: Thanks again, Marcella.

MARCELLA: All right. Goodbye. (hangs up)

MRS. DAVIS: Marcella Faye Davis! Look at you, you're soaking wet. Where have you been? And I've been trying to call home all afternoon and the line's been busy. Who in the world have you been talking to?

MARCELLA: (laughs) Oh, Mother, you'll never believe it!

Focus

1. Why did Bobby make the phone call?
2. How did Marcella find out Bobby's telephone number?
3. Why did Marcella want Cassy to talk to Bobby?
4. What did Marcella do to get help to Bobby?
5. Why was Mrs. Davis upset when she got home?

STUDY SKILL: Summaries

When Marcella's mother came home, she wanted to know what had happened. Marcella probably gave her mother a summary of the events of the afternoon.

A summary is a short way of telling about something. Good summaries give only the main points of a topic. Here are some ways to summarize the events in the story "The Phone Call."

1. Read the selection more than once.
2. Decide what the main idea is.
3. Make a brief note of other important ideas.
4. Leave out details not related to the main idea.
5. Use as few words as you can.

Read the paragraph below. Then read the three summaries of the paragraph. Check the rules for summarizing again. Decide which summary best follows the rules.

The telephone is an important means of communication. In an emergency, the telephone can help bring a doctor, the police, or fire fighters. A telephone call can also help you get information. You can learn the correct time, when a movie is playing, or what the weather will be. A telephone call can save time. In just a few seconds you can find out if a store has the product you want. You can also get help on your homework from a friend without leaving the house.

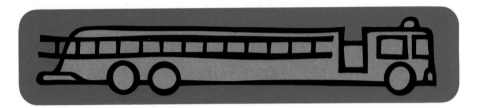

Summary 1

The telephone is important. The telephone can bring a doctor if you need one to help you. The telephone can bring the police if there is a robbery. Telephones can bring fire fighters if there is a fire. The telephone is also helpful if you want to find out something. You can call a friend on the telephone.

Summary 2

The telephone is important because it can bring help in an emergency, provide information, and save time.

Summary 3

The telephone is an important way to communicate. It can save time. It is handy to find out the correct time.

Here are some questions to answer about making a summary. Write your answers on a sheet of paper.

1. Which summary did you say was the best? Why?
2. Why are the other two summaries not as good as the one you chose?
3. What are the steps in writing a summary?
4. Think of a story you know. Write a summary of the story.

Discoveries can lead to inventions. An important discovery was finding out how to send a voice over a wire.

Alexander Graham Bell

ERNESTO RAMÍREZ

One day when Aleck was playing with his dog he wished his dog could talk. He took hold of the dog's jaws and moved them up and down. "This is the way to say how-do-you-do," he told the dog. "Can't you say it?" But the dog only wagged its tail and barked.

Aleck knew his dog would never talk. But he

wanted to learn about speech and sounds of all kinds. His mother was partly deaf, and his father taught speech at the University in Edinburgh. Even Aleck's older brother studied how sounds are made.

Mr. Bell was especially interested in teaching deaf children to speak. A child who is born deaf has no way of knowing what speech should sound like. Mr. Bell wanted to help deaf children learn to speak like everyone else.

Aleck also wanted to help deaf children. So when he grew up, he became a teacher like his father.

When Alexander was 23, his older brother died. His brother's death was a great sorrow to the whole family. Soon afterward, Alexander became very sick. Mr. and Mrs. Bell were worried about him.

"The weather is too cold and damp here in Scotland. Maybe a change of climate will help Aleck," said Mr. Bell. The family decided to move to Canada. Mr. Bell believed that in a better climate Aleck would get well.

The move across the ocean to Canada was a good one. Soon Aleck was well and strong. In a year the family moved from Canada to Boston, Massachusetts.

In Boston, Alexander continued teaching deaf children. He also helped other teachers learn about speech. And in his spare time he experimented with ways of making sounds with wire, magnets, and electricity.

One day Alexander showed a roomful of people

how he had taught a deaf child to speak. Alexander sat the child on a table. Then he sat in front of her on a high stool.

"Look at me!" he said quietly to the girl. The child looked into Alexander's face and watched his lips move.

Speaking slowly and carefully, he asked her a simple question. It was the same kind of question he would have asked any child. Then the little girl answered. She spoke aloud. Her voice had a strange, high sound, but it was a voice. The deaf girl was learning to talk!

The people in the room looked at each other with wide eyes. This is a wonderful thing, they thought. Young Alexander Graham Bell and the girl were talking to each other. The child was smiling. Her eyes sparkled with happiness. Alexander turned to the audience. "So you see," he said, "the deaf can learn to talk. They need not be lonely and unhappy."

Aleck continued teaching deaf children. Meanwhile, the father of one of his students became interested in Aleck's experiments with telegraph wires. The father's name was George Sanders.

"You need a better place to work in," Mr. Sanders said to Aleck. He asked Aleck to come live in Salem, where the basement could be made into a workshop for him. "You can still teach and do your experiments at the same time," Mr. Sanders said.

"Thank you," said Aleck. "I would like that. I need

more room for my experiments. My dream is to invent a way of talking over a wire. I know it can be done."

Once Alexander moved to Salem, he spent most of his time in his workshop. He had met a young man by the name of Thomas Watson. Watson was an electrician and could help Alexander with his experiments. Together they tried to send sounds over wires. But at first they had no success.

This was a hard time for Aleck. Many of his friends and relatives tried to discourage him. "It seems silly to think of sending sounds over a wire," one of them said.

Aleck refused to give up. "Many people used to say that it was silly to try to teach a deaf child to talk," he said. "If I can make a deaf child say words, I can make a wire say words!"

One day Aleck was in his workshop. He was working on the invention he called the telephone. Tom Watson was in another room connecting some wires. Suddenly Aleck heard a sound through his telephone. He rushed in to Watson.

"Don't touch a thing," he cried. "Show me what you were doing just now. A sound came through!"

Accidentally hearing this sound helped Aleck figure out a better way to try to make a telephone. But a year passed before his dream of making a good one came true.

One day Watson stood in a room working on a telephone. Aleck was at a telephone in a room in another part of the house. A wire ran between the two places. Suddenly Aleck tipped over a jar of liquid by mistake.

Forgetting that Watson was too far away to hear, Aleck called, "Mr. Watson, come here, I want you!"

All at once Aleck heard pounding footsteps. Then Watson dashed into the room. "It works! It works!" shouted Watson. "I heard your voice over the telephone. What a wonderful day this is! We have made a wire talk!"

Alexander Graham Bell's dream had come true. With the help of Thomas Watson, he had invented the telephone.

Focus

1. How did Aleck become interested in speech and sounds?
2. Explain what Alexander did to help deaf children.
3. Who was Thomas Watson? How did he help Alexander?
4. How was Bobby's mother in "The Phone Call" helped by Alexander Graham Bell?

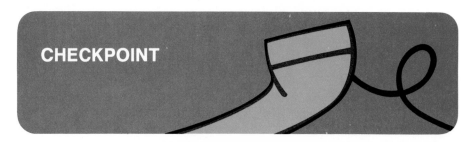

CHECKPOINT

Use the following words to complete the sentences below. Write the completed sentences on your paper.

discourage   narrator   detective
excitement   success   relative

1. Marcella used _____ skills to find out Bobby's telephone number.

2. The _____ of a play describes the scene to readers or the audience before the action begins.

3. Alexander Graham Bell's invention was a _____.

4. Alexander's failures did not _____ him.

Read each sentence below. Choose the word or words that make sense in each sentence. On your paper write the completed sentences.

invented   patiently   narrator   memorize   elderly

5. Before he _____ the telephone, Alexander Graham Bell taught at a university.

6. Bell and Watson worked _____ on their experiments to find a way to send sound over wires.

7. The _____ of a play tells the readers the details of the story.

8. Marcella wished that Bobby had been taught to _____ his telephone number.

9. Marcella asked the _____ woman who lived next door to call the police.

When someone says, "It's raining cats and dogs outside," are there really cats and dogs falling from the sky? Read each statement below. Decide which sentence tells you what the underlined expression really means. Write that sentence on your paper.

10. Alexander Graham Bell invented the <u>talking wire</u>.
   a. Bell invented a wire that carried sound.
   b. Bell taught a wire to talk.
   c. Bell invented a wire that could speak.

11. A flash of lightning <u>filled the window</u>.
   a. Lightning broke the window.
   b. The window frame caught fire.
   c. Lightning lit up the window.

12. Marcella <u>held her breath</u> when Bobby dropped the phone.
   a. Marcella waited anxiously.
   b. Marcella stopped breathing.
   c. Marcella didn't want to talk.

249

The telephone was one invention that brought people closer. The subway was another.

Subways
on the Move
DEBORAH KENT

It is Saturday morning. You are alone in the house when the phone rings. A friend of yours needs help. Her pet lizard has gotten out of the cage and is stuck

behind the stove. You'd like to help, but there's no way to get to your friend's house. Your parents are out with the car, your bike has a flat, and it's too far to walk. What would you do?

You would probably say that you'd wait for your parents to come home. But if you live in a big city you might not have to; you could take the subway. A subway would get you to your friend's house fast.

A subway is an underground railroad that travels in and around the city. People use subways as they use buses. The difference is that buses travel on city streets while subways travel in tunnels underneath the streets.

About twenty cities in the world have subways. The first city to have a subway was London. Workers dug tube-like tunnels and stretched miles of track in them. Today, Londoners call their subway "the tube." Some of the subway trains are so far below the ground that people get to them by using large elevators.

Many city people ride the subway to work or to school. There are times in the day when the subway stations get very crowded. Even large stations can be crowded around five o'clock in the afternoon.

At these large stations passengers can get something to eat at a small restaurant or food stand. They can also buy newspapers and magazines. Some passengers like to read while waiting for their trains.

The trains are powered by electricity. If the trains used gasoline, the tunnels would become filled with exhaust. Giant fans blow fresh air down into the subway. Stale air gets out through vents that lead to the street.

Subways were first built around 1860. At that time city streets were becoming jammed with horses and wagons. The inventors of the subway knew that the streets would be less crowded if some people traveled underground. The idea of the subway was a success.

But about sixty years later a cheap car was invented. As more and more people bought cars, the streets became crowded again.

Recently, the mayors of big cities have tried to solve the problems caused by cars. One solution is to improve old subways. Another solution is to build a new subway. Washington, D.C., and San Francisco are two U.S. cities that have new subways.

A few cities outside the U.S. have also built new subways. Mexico City has a beautiful new subway. It is sometimes called "The Miracle of Mexico City," but most Mexicans call it the Metro.

The people of Mexico City feel that their Metro is special. All the stations are clean and well lighted. Music plays from speakers built into the walls. Passengers can shop in stores and eat in restaurants.

Each station is decorated in a special way. Many stations have paintings and old photographs telling the history of Mexico. Some stations display the drawings of Mexico City's school children. Other stations have statues carved by Aztec artists more than 500 years ago.

Digging the Metro in Mexico City was like digging into history. When the workers began digging they discovered much about an early people, the Aztecs. Mexico City was once the capital of the Aztec nation. The Aztecs were great builders. They built a city of towering pyramids and great temples. When the Spaniards came and saw this marvelous city many of them thought it was the work of magicians. They believed no humans could build a city so beautiful.

But the city was ruined in a war between the Spaniards and the Aztecs. Later, Mexico City was built over the ruins of the ancient city of the Aztecs.

The workers who dug the Mexico City Metro uncovered many Aztec buildings. At one point the workers discovered a round temple that was completely undamaged. The temple had been buried since the time of the war between the Aztecs and the Spaniards. Mexicans are proud of their Aztec heritage. So the designers of the Metro decided to let the temple stay right where they found it. They built a subway station around the temple. Now passengers who stop at the Pino Suarez* station can see a temple that was built by the Aztecs hundreds of years ago.

Subways are efficient for moving people. They can also be interesting and beautiful places.

Focus

1. What is a subway?
2. For many years subways were not very popular. Why not?
3. Why are subways becoming popular again?
4. Who were the Aztecs?
5. Mexico City has a new subway that the people are proud of. Give three details describing the Mexico City subway.

*pē nō swä räs

It is easy enough, even fun, to ride a subway in your own city. But what if you were lost in a subway in a country where the people speak a language different from the one you speak?

THE TRAIN TO TOWN
RICHARD C. STEIN

"Juana, are you awake?"

Juana rolled over in bed. Who was that calling her? Then she remembered all at once. It was her cousin, Alicia.

"Just one minute," Juana called back.

"Okay, I'll be back in a minute," said Alicia.

Juana hurried to get dressed. When she first woke up she thought she was still at home in her small town near San Jose, California. Then she remembered: I'm in Mexico City! Last night Dad and I flew here to visit my aunt and uncle. Mexico City is *big* . . . especially for a small-town girl. . . .

While she dressed, Juana looked out the window. Her aunt and uncle lived in a high-rise apartment building that towered over a busy street called The Reforma. The street was lined with palm trees and had pink-tiled sidewalks. It looked very pretty, but Juana still wished she were back home. Big cities, she thought, were noisy, crowded, and confusing.

"Can I come in now?" Alicia asked on the other side of the door.

"Sure, come on in," Juana said.

Juana had met her cousin for the first time last night and liked her right away. Alicia was four years older than Juana, a steady, level-headed girl who seemed undisturbed by the size of this busy city. Well, thought Juana, it's her home; she's used to it.

"I've got a big surprise for you!" Alicia said. "My mother said we could go out together today by ourselves. So I'm going to take you to the very center of the city. It's a plaza called the Zocalo."

The center of the city, Juana thought. Already she did not like the idea—more noise, more crowds.

"Uh, how will we get there?" asked Juana.

"That's easy. We'll take the Metro."

"What's the Metro?"

Alicia smiled. "You know. The subway."

Oh no, Juana thought. She had never been on a subway before. But she knew subways were the most confusing part of any big city. She had seen pictures of them.

257

"Can't we take a bus?" Juana asked uneasily.

"Why should we?" said Alicia. "The subway is quicker and I think you'll like it."

I don't think so, Juana thought.

Juana and Alicia walked the crowded sidewalk of The Reforma. All around her Juana heard people talking in Spanish.

"How come you speak English so well?" Juana asked Alicia.

"Because I study it in school," her cousin answered. "Besides, I've always liked American movies. Westerns are my favorites. How come you don't speak Spanish?"

"Oh, I guess because we never speak it at home," said Juana. "My mother was born in the United States."

Juana stuck close to Alicia as they walked. What would happen if she got lost here? She wouldn't even know how to ask anyone the directions to get home. Home? Where was that? Her home was a thousand miles away.

"We'll cross the street here," Alicia said.

After waiting for the green light Alicia and Juana crossed The Reforma. On their right was a huge stone statue. The statue was called The Monument of

Independence. To Juana it seemed to tower over them threateningly.

Now on a smaller street they walked past stands where people stood drinking fruit juices. Other stands sold tacos, which were made out of meat and sauces all rolled into a tortilla. Shops displayed fruits and vegetables, some of which Juana had never seen before. It was all very exciting, but Juana missed her home town. The big city was so busy and crowded!

"The Metro station is right up ahead," Alicia said.

Juana gulped. This was what she had dreaded most.

Following a crowd, the two girls headed down a stairwell. The stairwell led to a huge hallway.

"We have to buy our tickets here," Alicia said, joining a line.

While waiting, Juana looked about her. The subway station was crowded with long lines of people hurrying in and out of clicking turnstiles. It reminded Juana of the shopping mall in her home town. There was even a little restaurant right in the station.

"I've got the tickets," Alicia said, holding two white stubs.

"This subway looks very new," said Juana.

"Oh, it's not so new. My father told me it opened when I was a baby," said Alicia. "The only problem with it is that it's too crowded. Come on. I'll show you the subway map."

They weaved their way through the crowd to a big map on the wall. The map was a diagram of all the stations of the Mexico City Metro.

"Here's where we are now," Alicia said, pointing to a station called Hidalgo. "We want to go three more stops to one called Zocalo. The Zocalo station is built on the very spot that was once the center of Aztec civilization. The Aztecs built a great city there long before the Spanish people came. There are interesting things to see right in the station."

Juana nodded. She tried to keep her mind on what Alicia was saying. "Are the trains as new-looking as the station?" she asked politely.

"Sure they are," said Alicia. "Just stay close to me in the crowd."

Alicia and Juana waited on the platform. Soon Juana saw the single headlight of the subway train speeding out of the tunnel. The train stopped in front of the waiting people and the doors snapped open.

"Let's go," said Alicia.

They stepped inside, the doors closed, and the train zipped away. It ran smoothly and silently. All the seats were full, so Alicia and Juana had to stand.

"Is there a subway in your town?" Alicia asked Juana.

"No. We walk, or ride our bikes, or drive in the car."

The train stopped at the next station where many people got on, and only a few got off. At the second stop a crush of people jammed into the subway car. Before she knew what was happening, Juana was being pushed to the middle of the car, away from the two doors.

Again the train picked up speed. Juana was uneasy. She was surrounded by a tight circle of people and she could hardly even move. Alicia said they were supposed to get off at the third stop. Then she thought of Alicia. Where was she?

"Alicia," Juana called. She spoke softly because she did not want to attract attention. "Alicia," she called again.

No answer.

Juana felt the train lose speed and stop. She

HIDALGO

squirmed through the crowd to look out the window. The sign outside said Zocalo. This was her stop. But where was Alicia? Then Juana noticed someone outside the window. Alicia! Juana could read her lips. She was saying "Juana, come out!" Just then the doors snapped shut and the train sped away.

The trip to the next station took only two minutes. But to Juana it seemed like one long nightmare. When the train stopped she followed the crowd out. The people hurried away from the platform, leaving Juana alone. She had never felt more alone in her life.

A tear squeezed from Juana's eye as she stood wondering what to do. She could try to get back to Zocalo station, but what if she couldn't find Alicia? Then she shook her head back and forth. Just be calm, she told herself. Be as level-headed as Alicia.

Juana decided to try to get back to the other station. Alicia would probably be there waiting for her. A small mishap shouldn't ruin her day. Juana turned to her right. She was in luck. On the wall was a big map of the Mexico City Metro. It was just like the one Alicia had shown her at the Hidalgo station.

Juana studied the map. A big yellow arrow pointed to a station called Pino Suarez. Over the arrow were the words *Usted esta aquí.** What could that mean? Then Juana smiled and said in a whisper, "I know. I'm in the Pino Suarez station right now." That meant Zocalo should be one station back. Juana followed the diagram back one station. Zocalo! She was right. Now all she had to do was get to the other side of the tracks to catch the other subway back to Zocalo.

Walking slowly, Juana followed a hallway, where she found an escalator going down. There she hesitantly joined dozens of other people going to another escalator. This one went up! Soon she was standing in a crowd on a subway platform. She saw a man dressed in a blue uniform. She wanted to ask the man if she was going the right way. But how do you ask someone a question when you don't know the language?

Finally she walked up to the man and pointed down the tracks. "Zocalo?" she asked.

The man nodded and pointed the same way she was pointing.

"*Sí, Zocalo*," he said.

*ū stāFH es tä ä kē′

Good, Juana thought. Everyone knew that *sí* meant "yes" in Spanish. Still, maybe she should ask once more.

"Zocalo?" she said again, pointing.

Once more the man pointed down the tracks. "*El Zocalo es las proxima. Mas para allá.*"*

I should have quit while I was ahead, Juana thought.

In minutes the train came and Juana stepped inside. At the next stop she got off. The sign said Zocalo. She had made it and across the tracks she saw . . . yes! it was Alicia, who had waited in her own calm way for Juana to reappear. The two girls waved across the tracks. "I'm coming!" called Juana over the noise, and Alicia understood. Juana followed the crowd along the way that seemed to lead to the other side of the tracks.

"Juana, thank goodness you're here." Alicia ran to her and wrapped her arms around her. "I've been so worried. I was just about to get on another train to look for you."

"Oh, it wasn't so bad," Juana said proudly. "I just read the subway map the way you showed me to."

Alicia's hands squeezed Juana's shoulder. "What a

*mäs pä rä ä yä′

smart cousin I have," she said.

Juana grinned.

Then Alicia showed Juana the subway station. In the subway station were models of the huge pyramids built by the Aztecs. Hundreds of years ago those pyramids towered above where this Metro station was.

Juana was calm enough now to study the models. "This is like a museum. It's like a museum right in the subway station."

"You're right," said Alicia. "It *is* a museum inside a subway station. Now let's go see the plaza. We can get something to eat. Juana, I'm glad you came to visit us."

Juana smiled and said, "So am I. Crowds aren't so bad after all."

Focus

1. Why did Juana go to Mexico?
2. How were Alicia and Juana going to spend their first day together?
3. What happened to Juana in the subway?
4. How did Juana find her way back to Zocalo station?
5. Both Juana and Marcella calmly solved a problem. Tell about the problem that each one faced.
6. At the end, how did Juana feel about big cities?

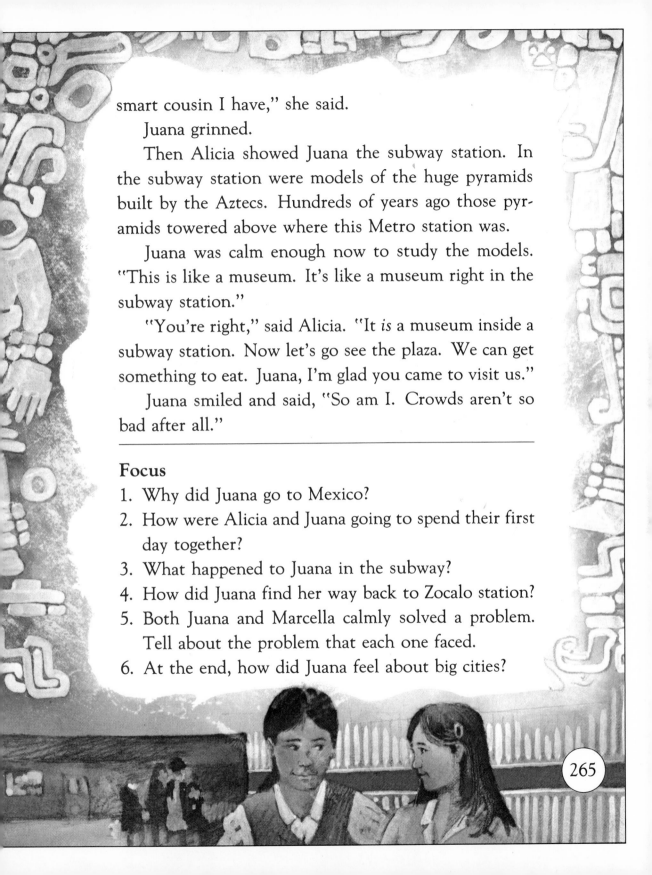

LIFE SKILL: Maps

Juana had to use a subway map to find her way in Mexico City. Would you know how to read a subway map? Most maps are similar to each other. If you learn to read a subway map you should have no trouble reading other maps.

Here is a map of a subway system.

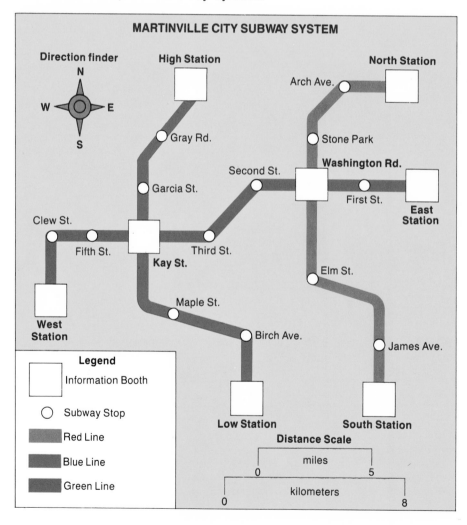

MARTINVILLE CITY SUBWAY SYSTEM

Maps use symbols to stand for real things. The symbols a map uses are explained in the map key. The key on the subway map tells the meaning of each symbol on the map. What does each symbol stand for?

A map also tells us things we need to know about places. Three things are directions, locations, and distances.

Directions

On most maps, north is to the top, south is to the bottom, east is to the right, and west is to the left. An arrow like this one $\overset{N}{\uparrow}$ shows which direction north is.

Distances

You find distances on a map by using the distance scale. The distance scale tells how many miles or kilometers are equal to one inch on the map. On the subway map, one inch is equal to 5 miles, or about 8 kilometers. North Station and Stone Park are 5 miles, or about 8 kilometers, apart.

Locations

You can tell from looking at the map that Arch Avenue is north of South Station. You can also tell that Fifth Street is east of Birch Avenue.

Use the subway map to answer these questions. Write your answers on a sheet of paper.

1. If you got lost in a strange city, how would a subway map help you?
2. Why does a map use symbols?
3. How would you use the key on a map?
4. How can you tell on a map which direction north is?
5. Suppose you wanted to take the Martinville Subway from South Station to North Station. How many stops would you make?
6. Use the subway map to find the distance between Kay Street and Gray Road.
7. If you were at the Fifth Street stop, where could you go for information?

267

CHECKPOINT

Vocabulary:
Word
Identification
Below are some new words you have learned. First write the vocabulary words on your paper. Then next to each word copy the correct definition.

1. efficient   traditions passed down
2. hesitantly   fumes from an engine
3. exhaust   win the interest of
4. dreaded   undecided, doubtful
5. heritage   without waste
6. attract   feared or worried about

Vocabulary:
Vocabulary
Development
(context clues)
Paying attention to the way words are used in sentences can help you learn new words. Read each sentence below. Under each sentence are four words. On your paper write the sentence using one of the four words in place of the blank.

7. Subways have been _____ in many cities because they are efficient for moving people.
   constructed   designer   train   roll
8. Alicia asked Juana to _____ her to town.
   friendly   accompany   companion   restaurant
9. In the shops the girls looked at all the _____.
   pried   crisp   merchandise   actively

Read the following paragraph and answer the questions below.

Comprehension: Cause and Effect

On Friday, Doreen's father bought a book about woodcraft. He knew that Doreen liked to make things out of wood. That evening Doreen looked at plans for a birdhouse, a scooter, and a bookcase. She had always wanted birds to live in her backyard, so she decided to build the birdhouse.

10. Why did Doreen's father buy the book?

11. Why did Doreen decide on a birdhouse?

Use the following map to answer the questions below. Write your answers on your paper.

Life Skill: Maps

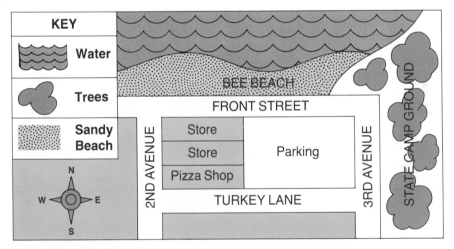

12. In which direction would you go to get from Turkey Lane to Bee Beach?

13. If you were at the beach and wanted to go to the State Campground, which street would you take?

14. The pizza shop is located at the corner of which streets?

269

Using the subway is a fast, convenient way to get around in large cities. Of course, when this country was first settled, there were no subways. How did people travel?

WAGONS WEST!

JEANNIE BARRON

Years ago, when pioneers were moving west across the United States, traveling was done by wagon. Even before people started to move to the good farmlands of the West, wagons were used for traveling and hauling.

The oldest kind of wagon was more like a cart than a wagon. The cart was made entirely of wood and had two large wheels. These wheels were made from oak logs. Not one nail was used in building the cart. It was held together by wooden pegs and ropes made from long, tough prairie grasses.

These carts were handy, but noisy. It was said that a person could hear them coming a mile away. The wheels creaked and groaned. They sounded like squealing pigs. Riding in one for a long way would almost make a passenger deaf. But the noise didn't seem to bother the two bulls, which were the usual beasts used to pull the cart.

French-Canadian traders in the northern part of the Old West used a kind of buggy. These buggies also had two large wheels, but the wheels had spokes rather than being made of solid wood. Without heavy wheels the buggies were lighter and easier to move. But they were still very noisy. One man said that the wheels could be heard for six miles. "It is like no other sound you ever heard in all your life and it makes your blood run cold."

The two most famous western wagons were the Conestoga and the stagecoach. These are the ones you often see in the movies.

Often a family leaving the East to seek a new home would travel part way across the country by riverboat. When the family reached Missouri, everyone would take the goods off the boat. Then the family would buy a Conestoga.

The Conestoga was used to carry families and their baggage. It was invented in the Conestoga Valley of Pennsylvania. The first Conestoga wagons were used on farms. The Conestoga was a large wagon. It had four wheels made of wood. The wheels had spokes and iron rims. The rear wheels were as tall as a man. The front wheels were smaller—only four feet high. Conestoga wagons were more comfortable to ride in than the earlier carts and buggies.

Over the boxlike wagon were curved ribs made of wood. Canvas was stretched over the wooden ribs. The canvas was painted or sprayed with oil to make it waterproof.

A Conestoga wagon could carry a lot. The heaviest things the family owned, such as stoves, plows, and big clocks, were stored at the bottom of the big wagon. On top of them came clothes and other light things. On the very top came things that were needed every day— food, water kegs, blankets, for example.

In the West the Conestoga was usually called "prairie schooner." A schooner was a sailing ship. Perhaps the sight of the canvas-covered wagons traveling on the wide prairie made people think of ships. Prairie schooners were built to cross rivers, too. The wheels would be taken off and the wagons would float like boats!

Prairie schooners traveled in groups of twenty-five to thirty-five. They were led by a guide called a wagon master or captain. He knew the trails to the Far West.

One type of Conestoga, called a freighter, was used to carry heavy supplies. Each could hold up to five tons of canned goods and bags of sugar, flour, and salt. Usually three wagons were attached to each other in single file. The last wagon, though, was small, and had only two wheels. It contained tools to fix broken wheels. The freighters were pulled by as many as twelve mules or oxen. When mules were used, the driver would sit on the left mule at the front of the lead wagon. This man was called a muleskinner. When oxen were used, a man called a bullwhacker would have to walk near the animals. As with the prairie schooners, the freighters usually traveled in groups. Fifteen miles was a good day's journey.

Travelers without families did not often go to the trouble of going west in prairie schooners. Instead, they chose to make the long trip by stagecoach.

The stagecoach was also called the Concord because it was made in a factory in Concord, New Hampshire. It was much more comfortable than a prairie schooner. The upper part or carriage of the coach rested on thick straps hung between the front and rear axles. This arrangement gave the coach a rolling motion.

As many as six passengers could sit inside the stagecoach. If need be, others could sit on top of the coach, or by the driver. From four to six horses pulled the coach along at speeds of five to nine miles an hour.

That's as fast as a steady run.

In stagecoach travel, there were stops every 15 miles at houses owned by the stagecoach company. There the horses would be changed and the passengers would walk around for exercise.

It was a long way from the East to California, Washington, or Oregon. Carts and buggies carried many people west. But the stagecoach and the "prairie schooner" were the most popular western wagons of all.

1. How was most traveling done in the Old West?
2. Describe the two most famous western wagons.
3. What is a schooner? How did the Conestoga wagon get to be known as a "prairie schooner"?
4. You have now read about subways and wagons of the West. Tell how traveling today is different from what traveling was like years ago.

Conestoga, Concord, prairie wagon—all were common in the Old West. Still, there was one kind of wagon quite different from any other.

High Wind for Kansas

MARY CALHOUN

High wind? Say, you don't know wind till you've felt the wind out west. Why, that western wind will peel off a section of the prairie and sail it away.

Well sir, there was one man who didn't just sit there hanging onto his whiskers. Once there was a man who harnessed that western wind. And this is how it happened.

One breezy morning back in 1853, some townsfolk were sitting in front of the livery stable in Westport,

Missouri. They were telling each other stories.

Suddenly Doc Taylor sat straight up like a bolt of lightning.

"What's that coming down the street?"

Whatever it was, it came scooting along in a cloud of dust, scattering chickens and trailing dogs at full yap. Out of the dust came a sail. A boat! A boat coming down the main street of Westport, Missouri!

The people ran out. The thing slowed to a stop. The dust died down. And there stood the strangest contraption Westport had laid eyes on yet.

It was a wagon with a sail. Not a covered wagon, but a wagon bed with a post up front for a mast and a sail rigged on it. No horses, no oxen to pull. No sir. That wagon had sailed down the street on the wind.

And in the wagon, his hand on a rudder-thing at the back, was a man. He was a short, wide man, bald on top, with a thick brown beard.

Ben Purdy, the wagonmaker, yelled, "Sailor, what do you have there?"

A voice rumbled up out of the brown beard. "What I have here, gentlemen, is—a windwagon."

The people roared. Why, this was the best fun they'd had in days.

The wagon fellow laughed along with them. But then he said, "You boys saw it move."

He jumped down and trotted alongside the men, around the wagon, telling them all about it.

"My name's Jones, and I made this thing," he said.

Then the wind started to blow, so everyone went into the livery stable where they could talk.

"Ladies and gentlemen," said Jones, "what have you got the most of? Wind. There it goes, just whistling by, not doing anyone a lick of good. Now, nothing's got a right to go around, not doing an honest day's work. I have a plan to use that wind!"

He explained his plan. He wanted to build a whole fleet of windwagons. People would go west in them. There would be no need for horses or oxen to pull the wagons, no need to follow the river routes for water for the animals. People would go west cheaper, and get there faster, sailing straight over the prairie on a forty-mile-an-hour wind.

Doc Taylor said, "What do you do when the wind doesn't blow?"

The beard shook with laughter. "When doesn't the wind blow?" Anyway, Jones said, windwagons traveled so fast, they could afford a calm day now and then.

Ben Purdy and others set a test for Jones. He was to sail his windwagon over to Council Grove, Kansas, 150 miles away, and then come back. They wanted to see how long it took him.

"Good stream flowing out there right now," said Jones. "Gentlemen, you're on!"

He hopped into his landship, let out the sail, and away he blew, beard pointed straight out in the wind

279

for Council Grove, Kansas.

"That's the last we'll see of that crank," said one of the men, laughing.

Next day the wind died down, and the men settled on the bench in front of the stable to joke about Mr. Jones and the windwagon.

A week went by. People had just about forgotten about Jones when along toward sundown the town dogs set up a bark. And there, rolling gently along on the breeze, came the windwagon.

Jones took in sail, pulled up to a stop, and jumped down with a paper in his hand saying that Jones had been in Council Grove a few days before. It was signed by the town blacksmith.

"I know that blacksmith, and he's an honest man!" Ben Purdy exclaimed. "Jones, you really did it!"

The people gathered around Jones and slapped him on the back. Were those men excited! They formed a partnership right away. The Overland Navigation Company, they called it.

And the wagon they built! It was huge.

Jones and the crew built their windwagon twenty-five feet long and seven feet wide. The wheels were twelve feet across, and the hubs alone were as big as barrels.

The whole town came to watch. At last it was done, ready for its trial run.

It was a good day for the test. Windwagon Jones

tied his beard down to his coat button with a string and hoisted himself up to the deck. "All aboard that're comin' aboard!" he shouted.

The partners climbed onto the deck. Windwagon Jones let out sail, but the breezes were still small, and the windwagon didn't move.

"Failure! Get a horse!" the crowd shouted.

Ben Purdy signaled the youngsters running around in the street. "Say there, put a shoulder to it!" A crew of boys pushed from behind. Jones spread out all the sail. A gust came, the wheels moved, and slowly the great wagon began to creep ahead. Down the dusty street it moved, picking up speed.

The people on board shouted and laughed it up to a hoot-n-holler. Windwagon Jones stood proudly at the back, steering the ship with the wagon tongue.

Now the wind worked up to full blow. Faster and faster the windwagon flew out of Westport up to thirty-five miles an hour.

About that time maybe Windwagon Jones should have taken in sail because the wind was blowing hard, but he didn't. He laughed and yelled with the rest of the people as the wagon bounced over the ground.

"Didn't I tell you it would sail?" Jones yelled. "Now watch this!"

Jones steered the ship into the wind. At first it came around in a grand sweep. But then the wind caught it sideways, turning the wagon and bringing it to a halt. Then it started running in reverse! After that the windwagon began to go around in circles.

"Steering gear's locked!" yelled Jones. "Take in sail!"

The men quit laughing. One after another, they all jumped off the wagon. They left Jones still yelling, "Take in sail!"

Soon the mighty craft was sailing around the prairie in mile-wide circles. The fellows could see Jones trying to take down sail and fighting his beard, which had popped loose from the string.

They say in Westport, Missouri, that no one ever heard tell of him again. But stories grew up on the plains, stories of a wagon that moved with a sail. Other stories told of a great bird with one white wing that flew the skies on black, windy nights. Why don't you look for yourself? Set yourself out on the prairie and watch. You might be the one to see Windwagon Jones come sailing by on the western wind!

Focus

1. What was a windwagon?
2. Why did Windwagon Jones want to build a lot of windwagons?
3. What test did the people of Westport set up for Windwagon Jones?
4. How did the test turn out?
5. What happened to Jones at the end of the story?

Buffalo Dusk

The buffaloes are gone.
And those who saw the buffaloes are gone.
Those who saw the buffaloes by thousands and
    how they pawed the prairie sod into dust
    with their hoofs, their great heads down
    pawing on in a great pageant of dusk,
Those who saw the buffaloes are gone.
And the buffaloes are gone.

CARL SANDBURG

Windwagon Jones was a dry-land sailor who had a dream. Christopher Columbus was an ocean sailor who also had a dream. Columbus's dream led to great discoveries.

CHRISTOPHER COLUMBUS

PIERO VENTURA

Columbus the Genoese

Christopher Columbus was one of the greatest sailors and explorers of all time. He was born in Genoa, Italy, in 1451. His father was a wool weaver. As a boy, Christopher helped his father at the loom.

Genoa was an important seaport, and Christopher dreamed of going to sea. While he was just a teenager, he left his family and joined the crew of a Genoese ship. By the time Christopher was 25 years old, he had made several voyages. He also had many stories to tell.

In 1477 Columbus went to live in Lisbon, Portugal. There his brother, Bartholomew, had a shop where he sold sailing charts and ship's instruments to sailors. Young Christopher met and talked to these seamen. He began to get ideas of his own about exploring.

By 1477 Portuguese sailors had made voyages far out into the Atlantic Ocean in search of new lands.

The Portuguese wanted to reach the Indies. (The Indies at that time included India, China, and Japan.) The sailors wanted to bring back treasures and spices to Portugal. They thought they could reach the Indies by sailing around Africa. Columbus believed that sailing around Africa was the hard way to get to the Indies. He was sure that sailing west would be a better plan.

The Departure

Columbus had a difficult time convincing people that his idea was correct. But after many years King Ferdinand and Queen Isabella of Spain gave him the money for his voyage. On August 3, 1492, his fleet sailed from Palos, Spain.

The *Santa María,* the *Pinta,* and the *Niña*

The names of Columbus's three ships were the *Niña,* the *Pinta,* and the *Santa María.* The *Santa María* was the largest, but it was also the slowest and it was hard to sail. Although Columbus set out in the *Santa María,* his favorite ship was the little *Niña.* He made the return voyage in the *Niña.*

All three ships were very small when compared with today's ships. All the ships were built of wood. They were crowded and uncomfortable. Each one had an upper deck, a quarter deck, and a hold. The captain's cabin was on the quarter deck. The cargo was placed in the hold.

The Crew

There were 90 people aboard the three ships. The *Santa María* had 40 crew members, the *Pinta* had 26, and the *Niña* 24.

Besides Columbus there were three officials on the *Santa María*. The captain was the most important person on board. The second in command was in charge of the crew. The pilot guided the ship and made notes on how far they traveled every day. The pilot also decided what kind of sails to use. Not everyone on board was a sailor. There were also a clerk and a police officer. In addition, each ship had a doctor. There were other important people on board. The boatswain was in charge of equipment. The storekeeper was responsible for the supplies. The caulker repaired cracks that often appeared in the hull. The cooper took care of the water barrels and metal parts of the ship. The others were plain sailors who had to do the most humble jobs.

Food for Sailors

Food was cooked on a wood-burning stove on deck. Most meals were dry. A sailor ate biscuits, salted meat, cheese, honey, rice, onions, almonds, and raisins. Each ship carried flour, wheat, and some barrels of salted sardines and anchovies. These foods did not have much vitamin C, which is found in fresh citrus fruits and some vegetables. So sailors often developed an illness called scurvy. This illness produced sores. It wasn't until 1795 that the British Navy started to give limes to its men to help prevent scurvy.

Life on Board

The men who made up the crew of the ship lived together for months. Without strict discipline and order, these men were likely to grow restless. So all work was carried out according to strict rules.

What was life like aboard ship in the time of Columbus? The sailors were divided into two groups of "watches." Every four hours the two groups switched. Half the crew ran the ship while the other half rested. Sleeping was difficult, because only a few of the officers had bunks. There wasn't even a special area for

sleeping. The sailors lay down on deck, in the open, without undressing.

A New World

After three weeks of sailing, the crew members wanted to turn back. But Columbus persuaded them to sail on.

Finally, on October 12, 1492, they sighted land—a small island in the Bahamas. Columbus landed on the beach and claimed the land for Spain.

Two Peoples Meet Each Other

On the next day, Columbus and his men met the Arawaks, the people of the island. Since Columbus believed that this island was part of the Indies, he called

the people Indians. The Arawaks were friendly, but Columbus could not understand their language. The Arawaks did not look like the people of the Indies that other explorers had described. Columbus had also been hoping to find great riches. The purpose of the expedition was to bring back treasure and spices. Columbus was surprised to see that these people had very simple possessions.

As soon as the ships had taken on fresh water, Columbus again set sail in search of the Indies.

The Coast of Cuba

On October 28, 1492, the ships sailed into a bay of what is now Cuba. Columbus thought that he had finally reached the Indies. He explored several harbors and sent men inland to look for Peking, a Chinese city. He hoped that the men could present a letter from King Ferdinand and Queen Isabella to the emperor of China. The men found no emperor and very little gold. Columbus had to settle for the beauty of the land. He wrote in his journal, "This world is the most beautiful I have ever seen, and I never get tired of looking at the splendid vegetation, so different from ours. I believe there are many plants and trees here that would be very much appreciated in Spain, but I am not familiar with them."

Columbus was right in thinking that Europeans would like these new plants. In years to come sailors brought back corn, potatoes, beans, tomatoes, and the cacao tree.

The End of the First Voyage

The voyage back to Spain was much more dangerous than the westward crossing had been. There were many terrible storms. The *Niña* almost sank. But Columbus finally arrived home safely on March 15, 1493.

Columbus went to Barcelona to give Ferdinand and Isabella a report of his adventures. They gave him a grand reception and named him "Admiral of the Ocean Sea." They asked him to arrange a second voyage and explore further.

Columbus did make three more voyages to America, but the first was the most important. On that trip he discovered what people in Europe called the New World.

Focus

1. When Christopher was a boy, what was his dream?
2. Why did Columbus want to reach the Indies?
3. Who finally gave Columbus the money to make the voyage?
4. Where did Columbus land?
5. Who were the Arawaks? Who did Columbus think they were?
6. How did King Ferdinand and Queen Isabella treat Columbus when he returned?

SOCIAL STUDIES READING: What's It All About?

Columbus convinced King Ferdinand and Queen Isabella to give him money for his trip. You can read more about the story in your social studies book.

Reading social studies books requires special kinds of reading skills. Here are some tips that will help you understand what you read.

TAKE A FIRST LOOK

Part of a social studies book is printed on the next page. First read the heading at the top of the page. It tells you what the page is about.

Now look at the picture. Read the words under it. What does the picture show you about the kinds of homes the king and queen lived in?

Notice the words printed in dark type. These are words that may be new to you. The meanings of these words are printed in the margin at the left.

FIND KEY IDEAS

Look down the page for clues to what the page will be about. Will it be about how the king and queen helped Columbus?

READ CAREFULLY

Read the page carefully. When you come to words printed in dark type remember the definitions you learned. Look for new words that do not have their meanings in the margin. Try to figure out the meanings of these new words from the sentences.

Notice the page referred to in parentheses. Sometimes social studies books will refer you to another page for more information about a topic. What do you think would be pictured on that page?

FERDINAND AND ISABELLA
Life at the Spanish Court

Ferdinand and Isabella lived simple lives for a king and queen. Except at parties, they ate little and wore simple clothes. They watched their spending closely.

The king and queen were very active in the affairs of the kingdom. They were always on the move. They traveled on foot and on horses and donkeys. When they could, they stayed at one of their many homes in Spain.

The homes looked grand but were furnished simply. When they traveled, the king and queen often had to sleep in tents.

Ferdinand and Isabella also had their pleasures. The king loved to hunt and to ride. Reading was the queen's favorite pastime. She owned more than 250 books.

Ferdinand and Isabella kept 40 musicians at **court** to entertain them and their friends. Sometimes they listened to **minstrels** sing ballads. (See picture on page 289.) They also liked to hear poets read their poems.

court: place where a king and queen live; also their followers.

minstrel: person who sings songs, ballads, etc.

293

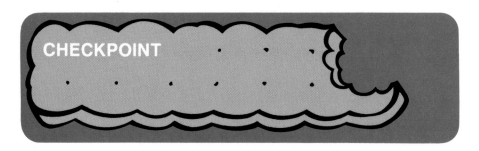

CHECKPOINT

Each word below is followed by three definitions. On your paper write each vocabulary word and its definition from the list.

1. contraption (gadget, canoelike boat, word made of two words)
2. journal (trip, group of people in court, daily account of events)
3. oxen (tools for cutting, male members of cattle family, kind of fish)
4. biscuits (boxes, foods made of vegetables, crackers)

Read the sentences below. Think about the meanings of the underlined expressions. On your paper write the sentence that tells you what each expression really means.

5. The sound of wagon wheels <u>makes your blood run cold.</u>
   a. The sound makes you angry.
   b. The sound frightens you.
   c. The sound makes you bleed.
6. Many families left the East to seek a new home <u>beyond the setting sun.</u>
   a. The families moved to the West.
   b. Many families traveled at night.
   c. Many families settled where the sun set.

7. A voice rumbled up _out of the brown beard._

   a. The brown beard talked.

   b. The brown beard had a deep voice.

   c. The man with the brown beard spoke.

8. People _roared_ at the windwagon.

   a. The windwagon made people laugh.

   b. People were angry at the windwagon.

   c. People acted like lions when they saw the windwagon.

9. The western wind is so strong it will _peel off a section of the prairie and sail it away._

   a. It is very windy in the West.

   b. The prairie is like a sailboat.

   c. The prairie is like a windy orange.

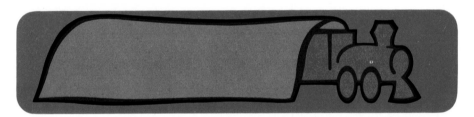

Below is a list of words using the prefix _mis-_ and the ending _-age._ First read the words. Then read the paragraph below them. On your paper write the paragraph filling in each blank with a word from the list.

Decoding: Prefix _mis-_, Suffix _-age_

| mistake | fortunate | misfortune | linkage | unlink |
| fortunately | linking | taken | unmistakably |

In the story "The Train to Town," Juana met with a __(10)__ . She was caught in a crowd while Alicia got off the train. Her troubles could have been worse. The __(11)__ between the cars of the train might have broken. The train might have been stuck in a tunnel. Instead, Juana got off the train at the next stop, remembered what Alicia had explained about the Metro map, and returned to the right station without making a __(12)__ . Juana stayed calm and used her head.

Stories in a Ch

Some stories are read, enjoyed . . . and forgotten. Others last and are read by grandparents, parents, and children. Those stories may be hundreds or thousands of years old and are like links in a chain.

In this unit the chain begins 2000 years ago in the days of the Greek legends. Next it moves on to Denmark of 100 years ago and the stories of Hans Christian Andersen. The last stories in the chain are by writers whose work children will probably read for years to come.

Each is a story to remember.

Scientists call spiders arachnids. The word *arachnid* comes from the name of the young girl of Greek legend—Arachne. Why did spiders get that name?

How the Spider Came to Be

JAMES BALDWIN

There was a young girl in Greece whose name was Arachne. All that she cared to do from morning till noon was to sit in the sun and spin silk and wool and flax. All that she cared to do from noon till night was to sit in the shade and weave.

Fine and fair were the things that she wove on her loom! Flax, wool, silk—she worked with them all. When they came from her hands, the cloth which she had made of them was so thin and soft and bright that people came from all parts of the world to see it. The people said that such beautiful cloth could not be made of flax, or wool, or silk. They said that the warp must be the rays of sunlight and the woof must be threads of gold.

Then one day Arachne said: "In all the world there is no yarn as fine as mine, and in all the world there is no cloth as soft and smooth, nor silk as bright."

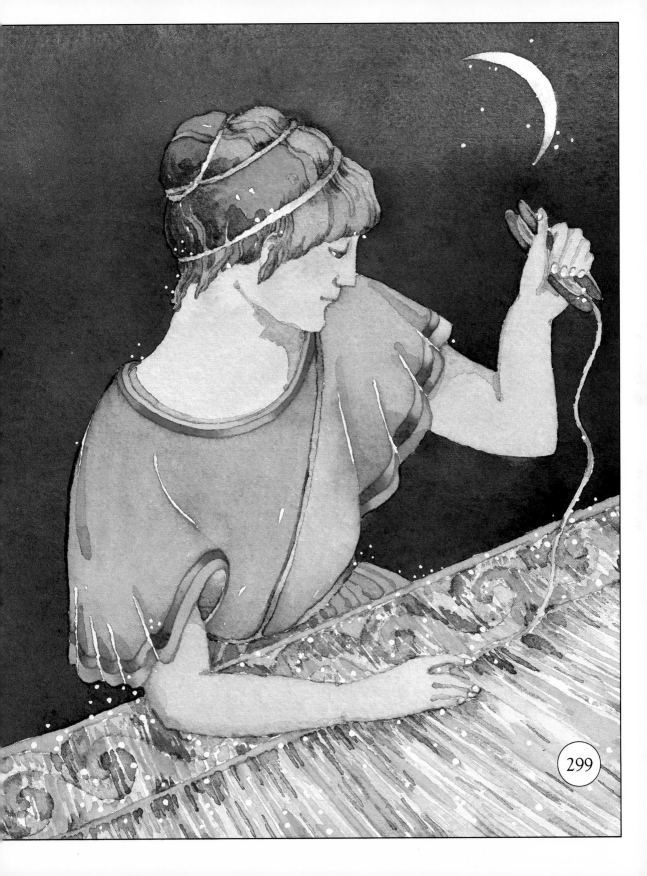

"Who taught you to spin and weave so well?" someone asked.

"No one taught me," she said. "I learned how to do it as I sat in the sun and the shade. No one showed me."

"But it may be that Athena, the queen of the air, taught you and you did not know it."

"Athena, the queen of the air?" said Arachne. "How could she teach me? Can she spin such skeins of yarn as these? Can she weave goods like mine? I should like to see her try. I can teach her a thing or two."

Arachne looked up and saw in the doorway a tall woman wrapped in a long cloak. Her face was fair to see, but stern, oh, so stern! And her gray eyes were so sharp and bright that Arachne could not look at her.

"Arachne," said the woman, "I am Athena, the queen of the air, and I have heard your boast. Do you still mean to say that I have not taught you how to spin and weave?"

"No one has taught me," said Arachne, "and I thank no one for what I know." She stood up, straight proud, by the side of her loom.

"Do you still think that you can spin and weave as well as I?" said Athena.

Arachne's cheeks grew pale, but she said, "Yes. I can weave as well as you."

"Then let me tell you what we will do," said

Athena. "Three days from now we will both weave, you on your loom, and I on mine. We will ask all the world to come and see us. Great Jupiter, who sits in the clouds, shall be the judge. And if your work is best, then I will weave no more as long as the world shall last. If my work is best, then you shall never weave again. Do you agree to this?"

"I agree," said Arachne.

"It is well," said Athena. And she was gone.

When the time came for the contest in weaving, all the world was there to see it. Jupiter sat among the clouds and looked on.

Arachne had set up her loom in the shade of a mulberry tree, where butterflies were flitting and grasshoppers chirping all through the day. But Athena had set up her loom in the sky, where the breezes were blowing and the summer sun was shining. She was the queen of the air.

Then Arachne took her skeins of finest silk and began to weave. She wove a web of marvelous beauty. It was so thin and light that it would float in the air and so strong that it could hold a lion in its meshes. The threads of warp and woof were of many colors, beautifully arranged.

"No wonder that the maiden boasted of her skill," said the people.

Jupiter himself nodded.

Then Athena began to weave. She took sunbeams

from the mountaintop, and snowy fleece from the summer clouds, and bright green of the summer fields, and royal purple of the autumn woods. What do you suppose she wove?

The web that she wove in the sky was full of pictures of flowers and gardens, and castles and towers. The web was full of people and beasts, and giants and dwarfs. It showed the mighty beings who dwell in the clouds with Jupiter. Those who looked upon it were so filled with wonder and delight that they forgot all about the beautiful web that Arachne had woven. Arachne herself was ashamed and afraid when she saw it. She hid her face in her hands and wept.

"Oh, how can I live," she cried, "now that I must never again use loom or spindle or distaff?"

Then, when Athena saw that Arachne would never have any joy unless she were allowed to spin and weave, Athena took pity on the young girl.

"I would free you from your bargain if I could. You must hold to your agreement never to touch loom or spindle again. Yet, since you will never be happy unless you can spin and weave, I will give you a new form so that you can carry on your work."

Then she touched Arachne with the tip of the spear that she sometimes carried. Arachne was changed at once into a spider, which ran into a shady place in the grass and happily began to spin and weave a beautiful web.

I have heard it said that all the spiders that have been in the world since then are the children of Arachne, but I doubt whether this is true. Yet, for all I know, Arachne still lives and spins and weaves. The very next spider that you see may be Arachne herself.

Focus

1. Who was Arachne and who was Athena?
2. Why was there a contest between them?
3. Describe the contest. Tell what would happen to the person who lost.
4. Athena won the contest, yet she allowed Arachne to go on weaving. Describe how Arachne could continue to weave.

The ancient Greeks were wonderful storytellers, as the tale of Arachne shows. Another of their stories is called *The Iliad*. This next tale is taken from that story.

WELCOME TO TROY!

GERALD GOTTLIEB

"They're gone! They're gone! The Greeks are gone!"

The news spread quickly in Troy. When people heard the happy shouting, they came out of their houses and stood blinking in the bright sunshine. Then they ran to the gates of the city. The soldiers allowed them to climb up to the top of the wall, where they looked with surprise at the empty plain.

The people of Troy were a little afraid to leave the protection of the city's massive walls. Some of the Trojan children had never been outside the walls at all. For ten long years the Greeks had been attacking Troy. They had been trying to rescue Helen, their queen. Helen had been kidnapped by a Trojan prince.

But now the Greeks appeared to be gone. Could the fighting really be ended? Had the Trojans won the long war after all? Were the Greeks really giving up their hopes of rescuing Queen Helen?

"A beautiful day for the end of the war—if it is the end," said a Trojan to his friend as they stood in the

304

crowd at the western wall. They laughed together nervously and looked around at all the people. All of Troy would soon be crowding up to the high ramparts of stone. Were the Greeks really gone?

"The King!" someone shouted. Old Priam, King of Troy, in purple robes and a tall purple hat, came walking slowly through the crowd. Tall soldiers of his palace guard cleared the way for him, their bright helmets flashing and their bronze-tipped spears held high. Priam looked serious, and a little sad. He had seen ten years of battle with the furious Greeks.

The old king came to the foot of the square-cornered watchtower next to the great city gate. The breeze stirred his white hair as he turned to face the anxious people of Troy. He gazed at his subjects for a long moment. The crowd stirred, murmured, then fell quiet. Only the sighing wind could be heard, blowing in from the sea.

Suddenly Priam, king of the Trojans, raised his hands high above his head. The wide purple sleeves fell back from his thin arms, pale in the sunlight. He shouted just one word.

"Yes!"

There was a moment of silence. Then a wild roar burst from the crowd. The people of Troy were laughing, screaming, dancing, and singing as they ran out of the gate and into the empty plain for the first time in ten years.

On the beach beyond the plain the people discovered the Horse. It was so big they wondered why they had not seen it from the walls of the city, three miles off. It was made of wood, painted bright yellow with a black mane. It towered high above the sandy beach, its black eyes staring. Why had the Greeks left it? the Trojans asked themselves uneasily. They walked around the huge horse, rapping the strong wood with their knuckles and wondering what it meant.

Besides the Horse, the Greeks had left nothing. The hated Greek ships, long and black, with red-painted prows, were no longer drawn up on the Trojan beach. The warlike Greeks had truly gone, and there was no sign of them anywhere on the sparkling sea.

But why had they left the great Horse of wood? What did it mean?

"It is a peace offering!" shouted a Trojan soldier. He wore a helmet and a breastplate of gleaming bronze. "The Greeks have lost the war and are fearful that the gods have stopped smiling upon them."

"Why stand here talking?" growled an archer. "Let us take it back to the city and celebrate."

"Back to the city!" shouted a young warrior, and the word leaped through the eager crowd like a spark in a field of sun-dried straw.

"Back to the city!"

So the joyous Trojans scrambled about the base of the bright-colored animal of wood, shouting and singing as they hauled the giant Horse to Troy.

When they had pushed their prize up in front of the city gate, the people of Troy paused. A white-clad figure, with dark hair streaming in the wind, stood atop the square watchtower. It was Cassandra, the daughter of King Priam.

"Trojans!" she called out. "Trojans, do not destroy yourselves!"

"Burn this evil thing!" she cried. "Burn it!"

But poor Cassandra's words were lost. The Trojans rolled the Horse through the gate and into their beloved city. Then the day was given over to gleeful dancing and singing. It was a happy time for Troy. The war was over.

The cold moonlight gleamed on the white stones of King Priam's palace. Within, everyone slept. Throughout all of happy Troy the people were exhausted from the long day's celebration. The only sound was the flapping of a flag in the wind that never stopped blowing across Troy from the sea.

The Horse stood in the darkness of the palace courtyard. All was still in the courtyard of Priam's great palace.

Suddenly the stillness was broken by a creaking sound, like that of a door being swung open on stiff hinges of leather. Silence again. Then a slight noise; and from the broad underbelly of the Horse a thick rope fell. It hung twisting and turning in the half-light,

its end reaching almost to the ground.

The rope had been dropped from a trap door in the Horse's body. Then a pair of legs came into view as a man began to lower himself quickly down the rope, hand over hand. The legs came swiftly toward the ground, and the pale moonlight fell upon them. Above the right knee glistened a long scar. The knee and the scar belonged to Ulysses.

Ulysses was a great Greek warrior. A polished helmet covered his red hair, and he wore the full armor of battle. He dropped lightly to the ground and darted into the shadow against one of the legs of the Horse.

All was peaceful. Ulysses stepped back toward the swaying rope, sheathed his sword, and looked up. Down from the hollow Horse came other Greek soldiers. In the black shadows outside the city gate, the other Greek chieftains waited impatiently.

"This silence pleases me not," grumbled a Greek captain. "It could be a trap. Might not Ulysses and his men have been discovered and taken prisoner while we were bringing our fleet back here?"

"It is a risk we must face," came the reply from another Greek captain waiting there in the shadows. The two looked out past the army to the moonlit beach where their soldiers had landed quietly in their black ships.

Suddenly a great shout split the night. It came from somewhere inside Troy. For a moment the chiefs stared at each other in puzzled silence. "What does that mean?" whispered one of the Greek chiefs.

The other chief shot out a long arm and clutched his friend's shoulder. "Listen!" he hissed.

Somewhere inside the gate there was the sound of clattering footsteps. The Greek chiefs stepped back into the shadows.

The massive city gate slowly began to creak open. The Greek soldiers in the front ranks crouched behind their shields. Every Greek held his breath.

It was Ulysses. He stood in the gateway. Behind him were the other Greek warriors, and beyond them the flames of a great fire could be seen.

"Welcome to Troy!" said Ulysses.

The Greek army gave one hoarse battle cry and then swarmed through the open gate. "Troy is ours at last!" shouted the Greek soldiers as they burned the city to the ground.

When the battle was over, the Greeks rescued Helen and took her home. A clever idea and a great wooden horse had ended ten years of war.

Focus

1. At the beginning of the story, why were the Trojans so happy?
2. What trick did the Greeks use against Troy?
3. Who was Ulysses?
4. What happened in the final battle?

SOCIAL STUDIES READING: What's It All About?

You just read a story about Greece and Troy of long ago. You can learn from your social studies book about Greece as it is today. Here are some tips to help you understand what you read.

TAKE A FIRST LOOK

Notice the main heading at the top of the page. This tells you what the page is about. Next look at the title under the map. This tells you what is on the map.

Do you see the headings in dark type above each paragraph? These headings tell you what the main idea of the paragraph is going to be. How many main ideas will you find on the page?

FIND KEY IDEAS

Read the paragraph headings. What are you going to learn about Greece? Now read the words printed in blue on the map. These are the names of bodies of water. Read the words printed in large black type. These are the names of the big cities and islands of Greece. Read the words in small black type. These are the names of the smaller islands of Greece. The map will help you understand the main ideas in the paragraphs on Greece.

READ CAREFULLY

Now read the page carefully. Look for the details that support the main ideas. Are there any unfamiliar words? Use other words in the sentences to help you get the meanings of these words. Find on the map those places mentioned in the text. You may need to read the page more than once to understand and remember all the ideas. Write the main ideas and list a few details that support each main idea.

FACTS ABOUT GREECE

Greece Is A Peninsula

Greece is surrounded on three sides by water. The Ionian Sea is to the west and the Aegean Sea is to the east. What sea is to the south of Greece?

Farming

There are nine million people to feed in Greece, but only half the land is good for farming. Also, the weather during the summer is very hot and dry. Today, as in the past, the people of Greece depend on other countries for much of their food.

Sea Trade

The coastlines of Greece are jagged and have many bays and harbors. The harbors are full of large ships. The Greeks sell to other countries such farm products as raisins, olive oil, textiles, fertilizers, and minerals. In exchange for these products the Greeks receive products they need. This is called trading.

313

CHECKPOINT

Read the story below. On your paper write the word from the list that best completes each sentence.

boast   loom   bargain   clutched

armor   maiden   ashamed   sheathed

Arachne was a **(1)** from Greece. She weaved beautiful cloth. People came from all over the world to see the work she did on her **(2)**. Arachne said that no one else could spin as well as she did. This **(3)**. led to a spinning contest with Athena. The **(4)** they set up was that the loser would spin no more. Athena won the contest, but Arachne was allowed to spin—as a spider!

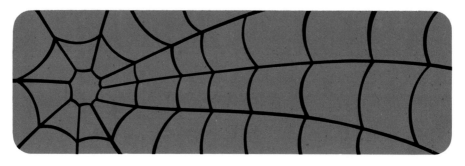

On your paper write the headings "Royal People," "Things Used for Weaving," and "Things Used in Greek Battles." List each of the following words under the correct heading.

flax   helmets   king

prince   armor   shield

loom   queen   spindle

5. Royal People

6. Things Used for Weaving

7. Things Used in Greek Battles

Read the following paragraph. Think what will probably happen next. Write the answer to the question on your paper.

On her way to the library Mary noticed a little boy. He was sitting on the curb, crying. "Are you lost?" Mary asked, but the little boy didn't answer. He kept crying. Mary found his name and address written on a tag in the collar of his coat.

8. What do you think probably happened next?
   a. Mary told the little boy to go home.
   b. Mary took the little boy to his home.
   c. Mary left the little boy and went into the library.

Below are some sentences with underlined words. On your paper write the correct meaning of the underlined word.

9. Arachne's <u>insistence</u> that she was the best spinner of cloth led her to lose the contest with Athena.
   a. not insisting
   b. act of insisting
   c. one who insists
   d. able to insist

10. Athena was Arachne's <u>opponent</u> in the spinning match.
   a. the act of opposing   c. one who opposes
   b. able to oppose   d. not opposing

11. Priam was a <u>resident</u> of the city of Troy.
   a. capable of residing   c. place to reside
   b. the state of residing   d. one who resides

315

The people of Greece were steadfast in trying to recapture their lost queen. This story is about a toy that is steadfast.

The Steadfast Tin Soldier

HANS CHRISTIAN ANDERSEN

Once upon a time there were twenty-five tin soldiers. They were brothers, for they had all been made out of the same old tin spoon. They stood at attention with "eyes front!" and wore the most splendid blue and scarlet uniforms.

The very first thing they heard, when the lid was lifted off their box, were the words "Tin soldiers!"

"Tin soldiers!" shouted the boy as he clapped his hands for joy. It was his birthday, and the tin soldiers had been given to him for a birthday present. Right away, he took them all out of their box and lined them up on the table.

They were all exactly alike—all but one. He was different, for he had only one leg. When the toymaker got around to making him, there wasn't quite enough tin left to finish him off properly. But he stood just as firmly on his one leg as the others did on their two. Of all these tin soldiers he's the one who became famous.

There were a lot of other toys scattered about on the table, and the most exciting thing of all was a lovely cardboard castle. You could look through the tiny windows and see into all the different rooms. Just outside the castle, some little trees were grouped round a piece of mirror that looked just like a lake. It even had wax swans floating about on it. You could see the swans reflected in the mirror's surface. But the prettiest thing of all was a lady who stood in the open doorway of the castle. She was made out of cardboard too. Her skirt was made of gauze, and over her shoulder was draped a narrow blue ribbon held in place by a large shiny pin. The pin was almost as large as the whole of her face, and it sparkled just like a diamond.

The lady was a dancer, so of course she was standing on one toe, with her arms outstretched. Her other leg was raised so high that the tin soldier couldn't even see it, so he took it for granted that she too had only one leg. "Just like me," he thought.

"What a wife she'd make!" he said to himself. "Only, I suppose, she's much too important. After all, she lives in a castle, while all I have is a box! And it doesn't even belong to me—there are twenty-five of us to share it. I'd never dare ask her to live there! All the same, I'd like to get to know her." He flung himself down full length, and hid behind a jack-in-the-box that was standing on the table. From there he was able to watch the lady, who kept standing on one leg without ever losing her balance.

Later in the evening the other tin soldiers were put back in their box. The people who lived in the house all went to bed. Then the toys that were left out began to play. Inside the box the tin soldiers were all rattling about. They would like to have joined the fun, but they couldn't get the lid off their box. There was such a lot of noise that the canary woke up with a start and began chattering away. But the tin soldier and the little dancer remained quite still.

Then the clock struck twelve, and suddenly the lid of the jack-in-the-box flew open with a bang and out popped a clown, just to scare everyone.

"Tin soldier!" shouted the clown. "Keep your eyes to yourself!"

The tin soldier pretended not to hear.

"You just wait till tomorrow!" said the clown.

Well, when tomorrow came, the children got up, and the tin soldier was moved over to the window sill. Now it might have been the fault of the clown, or it might have been a sudden gust of wind, but the window suddenly blew open and the tin soldier fell head-first from the third floor right down to the street below. It was a terrible fall! When he came to, he found himself with his leg in the air and the point of his bayonet wedged into the pavement.

The maid and the little boy rushed down into the street to look for him; but though they came so close to him that they nearly stepped on him, they couldn't find him. If only he had called out, "Look! Here I am!" they would certainly have found him.

Then it began to rain. The rain came down faster and faster and turned into a regular storm. When at last the rain stopped, two children came along.

"Look!" one said to the other. "There's a tin soldier. Let's send him for a sail!"

So they made a little boat out of an old newspaper, put the tin soldier in it, and off he sailed down the gutter. The two boys ran along beside him clapping

their hands. It had rained so hard that there were great waves in the gutter, and there was a powerful current. The paper boat rocked up and down, and twirled round and round till the poor tin soldier felt sick and dizzy. But he remained steadfast, never changed his expression, and gazed straight before him.

All of a sudden the boat swept under a plank that had been placed lengthwise across the gutter. It was terribly dark under there. It was like being in his box with the lid on, the tin soldier thought.

"I wonder where I'm off to now?" he said to himself. "If only the lady were here beside me, it could be twice as dark for all I'd care!"

Just then out popped a huge water rat who lived under the plank.

"Where's your permit?" shouted the rat. "Come on! Show your pemit!"

But the tin soldier made no answer. He clutched his rifle more firmly than ever. The boat rushed on and the rat after it. The rat ground his teeth ferociously and screamed out, "Stop him! Stop him! He hasn't paid his toll and he hasn't shown his permit!"

The current was getting swifter and swifter. The tin soldier could see daylight now at the end of the tunnel, but he also heard a dreadful roaring noise. The noise was enough to scare anyone. Just think! At the end of the plank, the water from the gutter gushed out into a great river. The tin soldier was in serious danger. If you can imagine being swept over a huge waterfall in a little canoe, you'll know just how he felt!

But by now he was so near the edge that it was too late to stop. As the boat shot out into the river, the poor tin soldier did his best to stand stiffly at attention. He wasn't going to give anyone the chance to say he'd so much as blinked an eye. The boat whirled round several times and was filled to the brim with water. It was bound to sink. The tin soldier was up to his neck in water and the boat sank deeper and deeper. The paper began to fall apart. Then the water closed over the soldier's head.

When the paper gave way beneath his feet, down he went. But at that very moment a big fish came along, opened its mouth, and swallowed him in a gulp.

My goodness, how dark it was inside that fish! Even darker than in the tunnel! There was scarcely room to breathe! Still, the tin soldier remained steadfast, while the fish leaped about and made the most terrifying contortions. Suddenly it grew quite still. Something like a streak of lightning seemed to flash through it— and then it was broad daylight. A voice called out, "The tin soldier!" The fish had been caught, had been

taken to market and sold, and was now in the kitchen, where the cook had just cut it open with her large kitchen knife.

She seized the tin soldier round the middle and carried him into the living room to show him off. There he was much admired. After all, very few people have traveled about inside a fish! However, he wasn't a bit conceited about it. The people in the living room stood him up on the table, and then he saw—really, life is quite remarkable at times!—he saw that he was back in the very same room he'd been in before. There were the very same children, and the very same toys spread out on the table. There was the lovely castle, and there stood the dancer in the doorway. She was still balanced on one leg, her other leg held high in the air, and her arms outstretched. The pin on her dress sparkled brightly. The tin soldier was deeply moved—he almost shed tin tears. He gazed at her, and she gazed back at him, but neither of them said a word.

Suddenly—for no apparent reason—one of the little boys picked up the tin soldier and threw him into the stove. The jack-in-the-box must have put the idea into his head.

The tin soldier stood in the bright glare and felt the

most terrible heat. The bright colors of his uniform were all streaked and faded, but whether this was the result of his journey, or the result of sorrow, no one could tell. He gazed at the lady, and she gazed back at him. He felt himself melting away, but he still stood there steadfast.

A door was suddenly opened, and there was a gust of wind. It snatched up the little dancer, and she flew into the stove straight to the tin soldier, blazed up into a flame, and disappeared. Then the tin soldier melted down into a little lump, and the next day when the maid emptied out the ashes, she found him in the shape of a tiny tin heart. But all that was left of the dancer was the shiny pin—and that was burned black as coal.

Focus

1. Describe the steadfast tin soldier and the dancer. Tell three or four details about each one.
2. How did the tin soldier happen to get out of the house?
3. Tell about two things that happened to the tin soldier outside.
4. How did the tin soldier get back home?
5. At the end of the story, what happened to him and the dancer?

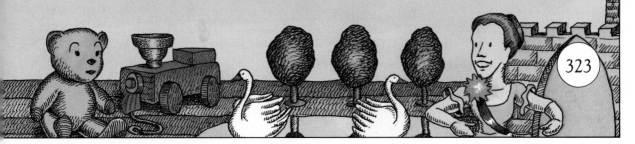

Hans Christian Andersen was one of the best known and best liked storytellers of all time. Today, in his honor, medals are given to the best authors and illustrators of books for young people.

THE HANS CHRISTIAN ANDERSEN AWARDS

PEGGY BRINK

The story of "The Steadfast Tin Soldier" was written by one of the best-known writers who ever lived. His name is Hans Christian Andersen, and he wrote nearly two hundred tales for children. He died more than a hundred years ago. Yet people everywhere still enjoy his tales.

The Hans Christian Andersen Medal is named after this writer. The Medal is an important award given to authors and illustrators of fine children's books. Thousands of new books for young readers are published every year. Few are good enough to win awards.

The Hans Christian Andersen Awards have been given every two years since 1956. One award goes to a writer and one to an illustrator. The awards are not given for a particular book. The judges choose the author and the illustrator who have published many excellent books.

Past winners are from many lands. They include Denmark (Andersen's home), England, France, Sweden, and the United States.

How are the winners chosen? First, publishers send the names of their best writers and artists to a jury.

The jury is made up of people from all over the world who know a lot about children's books. They read the books and talk about them. Then they choose the best writer and the best illustrator.

To win a Hans Christian Andersen Award is a great honor. The first American writer to win one was Meindert DeJong. He won in 1962. Mr. DeJong was born in the Netherlands, in a village by the sea. One day the wall that held back the sea broke. His village was flooded. But the people fixed the wall, and Meindert DeJong's family was saved. This event became part of one of his best-known books, *The Tower by the Sea,* an exciting story.

When Meindert was eight, his family moved to the United States, where his parents bought a farm. After he finished school, Meindert worked on the farm, but he knew he wanted to be a writer. After a long, hard day of work on the farm he would write stories, which he sold to magazines. Later he began to write books. One of his books is called *The Wheel on the School.* It is about schoolchildren in Holland who want to help bring storks back to their village.

Scott O'Dell is another American winner. He was awarded the writer's medal in 1972. Like Meindert DeJong, O'Dell won the award for all of his books for young readers. O'Dell was born in California. He was not always a full-time writer. First he was a cameraman. Then he worked on a newspaper. His very first book for young people is called *Island of the Blue Dolphins.* It is about a young girl who is stranded on an island for 18 years. Another book, *The Black Pearl,* is about a young pearl diver who finds a wonderful black pearl. Both of these O'Dell books were made into films.

Another award winner, Astrid Lindgren, was born in Sweden. She won the award in 1958. When she won the award, she said, "I want to write for readers who can work miracles. Children work miracles when they read."

Her most famous books are the Pippi Longstocking tales. Pippi is a young Swedish girl who lives without grownups. But she has a monkey and a horse to keep her company. With her two friends, Tommy and Annika, Pippi has many adventures. In one she is shipwrecked. In another she saves a child from a burning house. The Pippi Longstocking tales were first published in Sweden. Later they were translated into many other languages. They are favorites with children all over the world.

The Hans Christian Andersen Awards are given to writers and illustrators who have brought us stories children like to read over and over again.

Focus
1. What is the Hans Christian Andersen Award?
2. How are the winners chosen?
3. Who is Astrid Lindgren?

As you know, Astrid Lindgren won a Hans Christian Andersen Award for her books, which include the tales of Pippi Longstocking. The story that follows is one of those tales.

PIPPI
FINDS A SPINK

ASTRID LINDGREN

One morning Tommy and Annika came skipping into Pippi's kitchen as usual, shouting good morning. But there was no answer. Pippi was sitting in the middle of the kitchen table with Mr. Nilsson, the little monkey, in her arms and a happy smile on her face.

"Good morning," said Tommy and Annika again.

"Just think," said Pippi dreamily, "just think that I have discovered it—I and no one else!"

"What have you discovered?" Tommy and Annika wondered. They weren't in the least bit surprised that Pippi had discovered something because she was always doing that, but they did want to know what it was.

"What did you discover, anyway, Pippi?"

"A new word," said Pippi and looked at Tommy and Annika as if she had just this minute noticed them.

"A brand-new word."

"What kind of word?" said Tommy.

"A wonderful word," said Pippi. "One of the best I've ever heard."

"Say it then," said Annika.

"Spink," said Pippi triumphantly.

"Spink," repeated Tommy. "What does that mean?"

"If I only knew!" said Pippi. "The only thing I know is that it doesn't mean vacuum cleaner."

Tommy and Annika thought for a while. Finally Annika said, "But if you don't know what it means, then it can't be of any use."

"That's what bothers me," said Pippi.

"Who really decided in the beginning what all the words should mean?" Tommy wondered.

"Probably some professors," said Pippi. "People certainly are peculiar! Just think of the words they make up—'tub' and 'stopper' and 'string' and words like that. Where they got them from, nobody knows. But a wonderful word like 'spink,' they don't bother to invent. How lucky that I hit on it! And you just bet I'll find out what it means, too."

She fell deep in thought.

"Spink! I wonder if it might be the top part of a blue flagpole," she said doubtfully.

"Flagpoles aren't blue," said Annika.

"You're right. Well, then, I really don't know. . . .

Or do you think it might be the sound you hear when you walk in the mud and it gets between your toes? Let's hear how it sounds! 'As Annika walked in the mud you could hear the most wonderful spink.'" She shook her head. "No, that's no good. 'You could hear the most wonderful tjipp'—that's what it should be instead."

Pippi scratched her head. "This is getting more and more mysterious. But whatever it is, I'm going to find out. Maybe it can be bought in the stores. Come on, let's go and ask!"

Tommy and Annika had no objection. Pippi went off to hunt for her purse, which was full of coins. "Spink," she said. "It sounds as if it might be expensive. I'd better take along some money." And she did. As usual Mr. Nilsson jumped up on her shoulder.

Then Pippi lifted the horse down from the veranda. "We're in a hurry," she said to Tommy and Annika. "We'll have to ride. Otherwise there might not be any spink left when we get there. It wouldn't surprise me if the mayor had already bought the last of it."

When the horse came galloping through the streets of the little town with Pippi and Tommy and Annika on his back, the children heard the clatter of his hoofs on the cobblestones and came happily running because they all liked Pippi so much.

"Pippi, where are you going?" they cried.

"I'm going to buy spink," said Pippi and brought

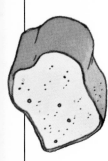

the horse to a halt for a moment.

The children looked puzzled.

"Is it something good?" a little boy asked.

"You bet," said Pippi and licked her lips. "It's wonderful. At least it sounds as if it were."

In front of a bakery she jumped off the horse, lifted Tommy and Annika down, and in they went.

"I would like to buy a bag of spink," said Pippi. "But I want it nice and crunchy."

"Spink," said the pretty lady behind the counter, trying to think. "I don't believe we have that."

"You must have it," said Pippi. "All well-stocked shops carry it."

"Yes, but we've just run out of it," said the lady, who had never even heard of spink but didn't want to admit that her shop wasn't as well-stocked as any other.

"Oh, but then you did have it yesterday!" cried Pippi eagerly. "Please, please tell me how it looked. I've never seen spink in all my life?"

Then the nice lady blushed prettily and said, "No, I really don't know what it is. In any case, we don't have it here."

Very disappointed, Pippi walked toward the door. "Then I have to keep on looking," she said. "I can't go back home without spink."

The next store was a hardware store. A salesman bowed politely to the children.

"I would like to buy a spink," said Pippi. "But I

want it to be of the best kind, the one that is used for killing lions."

The salesman looked as sly as a fox. "Let's see," he said and scratched himself behind the ear. "Let's see." He took out a small rake. "Is this all right?" he said as he handed it to Pippi.

Pippi looked indignantly at him. "That's what the professors would call a rake," she said. "But it happens to be a spink I wanted. Don't try to fool an innocent little child."

Then the salesman laughed and said, "Unfortunately we don't have the thing you want. Ask in the store around the corner that carries notions."

"Notions," Pippi muttered to Tommy and Annika when they came out on the street. "I just know they won't have it there."

Suddenly she brightened. "Perhaps it's a sickness," she said. "Let's go ask the doctor."

Annika knew where the doctor lived because she had gone there to be vaccinated.

Pippi rang the bell. A nurse opened the door.

"I would like to see the doctor," said Pippi. "It's a very serious case, a terribly dangerous disease."

"This way, please," said the nurse.

The doctor was sitting at his desk when the children came in. Pippi went straight to him, closed her eyes, and stuck her tongue out.

"What is the matter with you?" said the doctor.

Pippi opened her clear blue eyes and pulled in her tongue. "I'm afraid I've got spink," she said, "because I itch all over. And when I sleep my eyes close. Sometimes I have the hiccups and on Sunday I didn't feel very well after having eaten a dish of shoe polish and milk. My appetite is quite hearty, but sometimes I get the food down my windpipe and then nothing good comes of it. It must be the spink, which bothers me. Tell me, is it contagious?"

The doctor looked at Pippi's rosy face and said, "I think you're healthier than most. I'm sure you're not suffering from spink."

Pippi grabbed him eagerly by the arm. "But there is a disease by that name, isn't there?"

"No," said the doctor, "there isn't. But even if there were, I don't think it would have any effect on you."

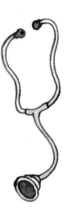

Pippi looked sad. She made a deep curtsy to the doctor as she said good-by, and so did Annika. Tommy bowed. And then they went out to the horse, who was waiting at the doctor's fence.

Not far from the doctor's house was a high three-story house with a window open on the upper floor. Pippi pointed toward the open window and said, "It wouldn't surprise me if the spink is in there. I'll dash up and see." Quickly she climbed up the water spout. When she reached the level of the window she threw herself heedlessly into the air and grabbed hold of the window sill. She hoisted herself up by the arms and stuck her head in.

In the room two ladies were sitting chatting. Imagine their astonishment when all of a sudden a red head popped over the window sill and a voice said, "Is there by any chance a spink here?"

The two ladies cried out in terror. "Good heavens, what are you saying, child? Has something escaped?"

"That is exactly what I would like to know," said Pippi politely.

"Maybe it's under the bed!" screamed one of the ladies. "Does it bite?"

"I think so," said Pippi. "It's supposed to have tremendous fangs."

The two ladies looked at each other with alarm. Pippi looked around curiously, but finally she said with a sigh, "No, there isn't as much as a spink's whisker around here. Excuse me for disturbing you. I just thought I would ask, since I happened to be passing by."

She slid down the water spout and said sadly to Tommy and Annika, "There isn't any spink in this town. Let's ride back home."

And that's what they did. When they jumped down from the horse outside the veranda, Tommy came close to stepping on a little beetle which was crawling on the gravel path.

"Be careful not to step on the beetle!" Pippi cried.

335

All three bent down to look at it. It was a tiny thing, with green wings that gleamed like metal.

"What a pretty little creature," said Annika. "I wonder what it is."

"It isn't a June bug," said Tommy.

"And no ladybug either," said Annika. "And no stagbeetle. I wish I knew what it was."

All at once a radiant smile lit up Pippi's face. "I know," she said. "It's a spink."

"Are you sure?" Tommy said doubtfully.

"Don't you think I know a spink when I see one?" said Pippi. "Have you ever seen anything so spink-like in your life?"

She carefully moved the beetle to a safer place, where no one could step on it. "My sweet little spink," she said tenderly. "I knew that I would find one at last. But isn't it funny! We've been hunting all over town for a spink, and there was one right here all the time!"

Focus

1. At the beginning of the story what did Pippi discover?
2. Pippi looked in different places to find an example of her discovery. Describe three of the places.
3. Where did Pippi finally find what she was looking for? What was it?
4. What does Pippi have to do with the Hans Christian Andersen Awards?

HELP!

Can anybody tell me, please,
a bit about the thing
with seven legs and furry knees,
four noses and a wing?

Oh what has prickles on its chin,
what's yellow, green and blue,
and what has soft and slimy skin?
Oh tell me, tell me, do.

And tell me, what has polka dots
on every other ear,
what ties its tail in twenty knots,
what weeps a purple tear?

Oh what is growling long and low
and please, has it been fed?
I think I'd really better know . . .
it's sitting on my head.

JACK PRELUTSKY

To find out what a spink is, Pippi and her friends go to different shops looking for one.

Suppose that in one of these shops Pippi finds another interesting word, *ribble.* Ribble is a new food Pippi wants to know more about, so she reads the directions for cooking ribble.

The directions might look like this:

RIBBLE
Cooking Directions

To make:		Use:			
Servings	Cups Cooked Ribble	Ribble	Water	Salt	Butter or Margarine
2	1⅓	1 cup	¾ cup	¼ tsp.	½ tbs.
4	2⅔	2 cups	1⅔ cups	½ tsp.	1 tbs.
8	5	4 cups	3 cups	1 tsp.	2 tbs.

1. Stir together in a saucepan ribble, salt, and butter or margarine.
2. Bring to a fast boil.
3. Reduce heat. Cover and cook until all water is gone (about 5 minutes).

For firmer ribble, use less water.

Following directions step by step can be very important. If you are cooking something, your dish can end in failure if you leave out a step. It is also important to do the steps in the correct order.

What do you think might happen if you forget the water in cooking ribble?

See if you can answer these questions. Write your answers on a sheet of paper.

1. How would you know how much ribble to cook for 2 servings? What amount is it?
2. Suppose you have only $\frac{1}{2}$ tablespoon of butter. How much ribble can you cook?
3. Which step in the directions tells you how long to cook ribble?
4. Why is it important to follow directions step by step?
5. How can pictures help you follow directions?
6. Make up a dish that the people of Troy might have eaten. You can give it an original name. Tell how to make it. Be sure to list the steps in the right order.

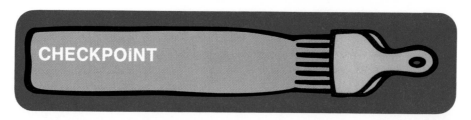

CHECKPOINT

Below are some new words you have learned. First write the vocabulary words on your paper. Then next to each word copy the correct definition.

1. innocent   put into another language
2. scarlet   easy to see or understand
3. author   free from guilt
4. peculiar   one who writes books
5. apparent   very bright red
6. translated   strange or odd

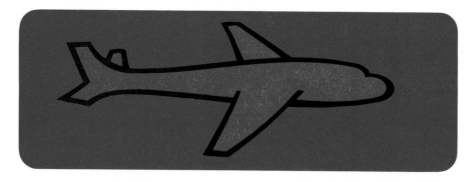

When writing stories authors don't always tell everything. The reader has to make some guesses. Read the paragraph below. Think about the details or ideas that were not written. Then answer question 7.

On Sunday Paula is going to visit her grandfather. It will be her first plane trip alone. Her tickets are in her desk. Twice a day, at least, Paula checks her desk for the tickets. She has also taken a book out of the library that explains how planes work. When she grows up Paula hopes to become a pilot.

7. According to the story, which sentence is most likely true?

    a. Paula's grandfather is a farmer.

    b. Paula is afraid of planes.

    c. Paula is excited about the trip.

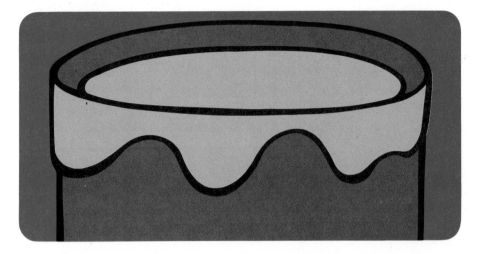

Read the following label. Use the information on the label to answer the questions below. Write the answers on your paper.

Life Skill: Directions

POWDERED PAINT

EASY TO USE. Perfect for painting pictures or surfaces of wooden objects.

Directions: For every three tablespoons of paint add one tablespoon water. Mix well for about 2 minutes until paint is thick and smooth. The paint will then be ready to use. For wooden surfaces, two coats should be applied.

8. How much paint will you use for every tablespoon of water?

9. If you were painting a wooden chair, how many coats of paint should you apply?

10. Besides wooden objects, what can this paint be used for?

Pippi Longstocking is a made-up person. So are her adventures. Laura Wilder's adventures are based on real people and real events.

PRAIRIE WINTER
PART 1 LAURA INGALLS WILDER

Mary and Laura and Carrie were all enjoying school so much that they were sorry when Saturday and Sunday interrupted it. They looked forward to Monday. But when Monday came, Laura was cross because her red flannel underwear was so hot and scratchy.

It made her back itch, and her neck, and her wrists, and where it was folded around her ankles, under her stockings and shoe-tops, that red flannel almost drove her crazy.

At noon she begged Ma to let her change to cooler underthings. "It's too hot for my red flannels, Ma!" she protested.

"I know the weather's turned warm," Ma answered gently. "But this is the time of year to wear flannels, and you would catch cold if you took them off."

Laura went crossly back to school and sat squirming because she must not scratch. She held the flat geography book open before her, but she wasn't studying. She was trying to bear the itching flannels and wanting to get home where she could scratch. The sun-

343

shine from the western windows had never crawled so slowly.

Suddenly there was no sunshine. It went out, as if someone had blown out the sun like a lamp. The outdoors was gray, the windowpanes were gray, and at the same moment a wind crashed against the schoolhouse, rattling windows and doors and shaking the walls.

Miss Garland started up from her chair. One of the little Beardsley girls screamed and Carrie turned white.

Laura thought, "It happened this way on Plum Creek, the Christmas when Pa was lost." Her whole heart hoped and prayed that Pa was safe at home now.

Teacher and all the others were staring at the windows, where nothing but grayness could be seen. They all looked frightened. Then Miss Garland said, "It is only a storm, children. Go on with your lessons."

The blizzard was scouring against the walls, and the winds squealed and moaned in the stovepipe.

All the heads bent over the books as Teacher had told them to do. But Laura was trying to think how to get home. The schoolhouse was a long way from Main Street, and there was nothing to guide them.

All the others had come from the East that summer. They had never seen a prairie blizzard. But Laura and Carrie knew what it was. Carrie's head was bowed limply above her book, and the back of it, with the white parting between the braids of fine, soft hair, looked small and helpless and frightened.

There was only a little fuel at the schoolhouse. The

school board was buying coal, but only one load had been delivered. Laura thought they might outlive the storm in the schoolhouse, but they could not do it without burning all the costly patent desks.

Without lifting her head, Laura looked up at Teacher. Miss Garland was thinking and biting her lip. She could not decide to dismiss school because of a storm, but this storm frightened her.

"I ought to tell her what to do," Laura thought. But she could not think what to do. It was not safe to leave the schoolhouse and it was not safe to stay there. Even the twelve patent desks might not last long enough to keep them warm until the blizzard ended. She thought of her wraps and Carrie's, in the entry. Whatever happened she must somehow keep Carrie warm. Already the cold was coming in.

There was a loud thumping in the entry. Every pupil started and looked at the door.

It opened and a man stumbled in. He was bundled in overcoat, cap, and muffler, all solid white with snow driven into the woolen cloth. They could not see who he was until he pulled down the stiffened muffler.

"I came out to get you," he told Teacher.

He was Mr. Foster, the man who owned the ox team and had come in from his claim to stay in town for the winter at Sherwood's, across the street from Teacher's house.

Miss Garland thanked him. She rapped her ruler on

the desk and said, "Attention! School is dismissed. You may bring your wraps from the entry and put them on by the stove."

Laura said to Carrie, "You stay here. I'll bring your wraps."

The entry was freezing cold; snow was blowing in between the rough boards of the walls. Laura was chilled before she could snatch her coat and hood from their nail. She found Carrie's and carried the armful into the schoolhouse.

Crowded around the stove, they all put on their wraps and fastened them snugly. Cap Garland did not smile. His blue eyes narrowed and his mouth set straight while Mr. Foster talked.

Laura wrapped the muffler snugly over Carrie's white face and took firm hold of her mittened hand. She told Carrie, "Don't worry, we'll be all right."

"Now, just follow me," said Mr. Foster, taking Teacher's arm. "And keep close together."

He opened the door, and led the way with Miss Garland. Mary Power and Minnie each took one of the little Beardsley girls. Ben and Arthur followed them closely, then Laura went out with Carrie into blinding snow. Cap shut the door behind them.

They could hardly walk in the beating, whirling wind. The schoolhouse had disappeared. They could see nothing but swirling whiteness and snow and then a glimpse of each other, disappearing like shadows.

Laura felt that she was smothering. The icy particles of snow whirled scratching into her eyes and smothered her breathing. Her skirts whipped around her, now wrapped so tightly that she could not step, then whirled and lifted to her knees. Suddenly tightening, they made her stumble. She held tightly to Carrie, and Carrie, struggling and staggering, was pulled away by the wind and then flung back against her.

"We can't go on this way," Laura thought. But they had to.

She was alone in the confusion of whirling winds and snow except for Carrie's hand that she must never let go. The winds struck her this way and that. She could not see nor breathe, she stumbled and was falling, then suddenly she seemed to be lifted and Carrie bumped against her. She tried to think. The others must be somewhere ahead. She must walk faster and keep up with them or she and Carrie would be lost. If they were lost on the prairie they would freeze to death.

But perhaps they were all lost. Main Street was only two blocks long. If they were going only a little way to north or south they would miss the block of stores, and beyond was empty prairie for miles.

Laura thought they must have gone far enough to reach Main Street, but she could see nothing.

The storm thinned a little. She saw shadowy figures ahead. They were darker gray in the whirling gray-whiteness. She went on as fast as she could, with

Carrie, until she touched Miss Garland's coat.

They had all stopped. Huddled in their wraps, they stood like bundles close together in the swirling mist. Teacher and Mr. Foster were trying to talk, but the winds confused their shouts so that no one could hear what they said. Then Laura began to know how cold she was.

Her mittened hand was so numb that it hardly felt Carrie's hand. She was shaking all over and deep inside her there was a shaking that she could not stop. Only in her very middle there was a solid knot that ached, and her shaking pulled this knot tighter so that the ache grew worse.

She was frightened about Carrie. The cold hurt too much, Carrie could not stand it. Carrie was so little and thin, she had always been delicate, she could not stand such cold much longer. They must reach shelter soon.

Focus

1. Where does the first part of the story take place?
2. Describe what it was like when the storm hit.
3. Why was Laura worried about Carrie?
4. Who was Mr. Foster? Why did he come to the school?
5. Why was walking in the blizzard so hard and dangerous?
6. What do you think will happen next?

PRAIRIE WINTER
PART 2 LAURA INGALLS WILDER

Mr. Foster and Teacher were moving again, going a little to the left. All the others stirred and hurried to follow them. Laura took hold of Carrie with her other hand, which had been in her coat pocket and was not quite so numb, and then suddenly she saw a shadow go by them. She knew it was Cap Garland.

He was not following the others to the left. With hands in his pockets and head bent, he went trudging straight ahead into the storm. A fury of winds thickened the air with snow and he vanished.

Laura did not dare follow him. She must take care of Carrie and Teacher had told them to follow her. She was sure that Cap was going toward Main Street, but perhaps she was mistaken and she could not take Carrie away from the others.

She kept tight hold of Carrie and hurried to follow Mr. Foster and Teacher as fast as she could. Her chest sobbed for air and her eyes strained open in the icy snow-particles that hurt them like sand. Carrie struggled bravely, stumbling and flopping, doing her best to stay on her feet and keep on going. Only for instants when the snow-whirl was thinner could they glimpse the shadows moving ahead of them.

Laura felt that they were going in the wrong direction. She did not know why she felt so. No one could see anything. There was nothing to go by—no sun, no sky, no direction in the winds blowing fiercely from all directions. There was nothing but the dizzy whirling and the cold.

It seemed that the cold and the winds, the noise of the winds and the blinding, smothering, scratching snow, and the effort and the aching, were forever. Pa had lived through three days of a blizzard under the bank of Plum Creek. But there were no creek banks here. Here there was nothing but bare prairie. Pa had told about sheep caught in a blizzard, huddled together under the snow. Some of them had lived. Perhaps people could do that, too. Carrie was too tired to go much farther, but she was too heavy for Laura to carry. They must go on as long as they could, and then. . . .

Then, out of the whirling whiteness, something hit her. The hard blow crashed against her shoulder and all through her. She rocked on her feet and stumbled against something solid. It was high, it was hard, it was the corner of two walls. Her hands felt it, her eyes saw it. She had walked against some building.

With all her might she yelled, "Here! Come here! Here's a house!"

All around the house the winds were howling so that at first no one heard her. She pulled the icy stiff muffler from her mouth and screamed into the blinding storm. At last she saw a shadow in it, two tall shadows thinner than the shadowy wall she clung to—Mr. Foster and Teacher. Then other shadows pressed close around her.

No one tried to say anything. They crowded together and they were all there—Mary Power and Minnie, each with a little Beardsley girl, and Arthur Johnson and Ben Woodworth with the small Wilmarth boys. Only Cap Garland was missing.

They followed along the side of that building till they came to the front of it, and it was Mead's Hotel, at the very north end of Main Street.

Beyond it was nothing but the railroad track covered with snow, the lonely depot and the wide, open prairie. If Laura had been only a few steps nearer the others, they would all have been lost on the endless prairie north of town.

For a moment they stood by the hotel's lamplit windows. Warmth and rest were inside the hotel, but the blizzard was growing worse and they must all reach home.

Main Street would guide all of them except Ben Woodworth. No other buildings stood between the

hotel and the depot where he lived. So Ben went into the hotel to stay till the blizzard was over. He could afford to do that because his father had a regular job.

Minnie and Arthur Johnson, taking the little Wilmarth boys, had only to cross Main Street to Wilmarth's grocery store and their home was beside it. The others went on down Main Street, keeping close to the buildings. They passed the saloon, they passed Royal Wilder's feed store, and then they passed Barker's grocery. The Beardsley Hotel was next and there the little Beardsley girls went in.

The journey was almost ended now. They passed Couse's Hardware store and they crossed Second Street to Fuller's Hardware. Mary Power had only to pass the drugstore now. Her father's tailor shop stood next to it.

Laura and Carrie and Teacher and Mr. Foster had to cross Main Street now. It was a wide street. But if they missed Pa's house, the haystacks and the stable were still between them and the open prairie.

They did not miss the house. One of its lighted windows made a glow that Mr. Foster saw before he ran into it. He went on around the house corner with Teacher to go by the clothesline, the haystacks, and the stable to the Garland house.

Laura and Carrie were safe at their own front door. Laura's hands fumbled at the doorknob, too stiff to turn it. Pa opened the door and helped them in.

He was wearing overcoat and cap and muffler. He had set down the lighted lantern and dropped a coil of rope. "I was just starting out after you," he said.

In the still house Laura and Carrie stood, taking deep breaths. It was so quiet there where the winds did not push and pull at them. They were still blinded, but the whirling icy snow had stopped hurting their eyes.

Laura felt Ma's hands breaking away the icy muffler, and she said, "Is Carrie all right?"

"Yes, Carrie's all right," said Pa.

Ma took off Laura's hood and unbuttoned her coat and helped her pull out of its sleeves. "These wraps are driven full of ice," Ma said. They crackled when she shook them and little drifts of whiteness sifted to the floor.

"Well," Ma said, " 'All's well that ends well.' You're not frostbitten. You can go to the fire and get warm."

Laura could hardly move but she stooped and with her fingers dug out the caked snow that the wind had driven in between her woolen stockings and the tops of her shoes. Then she staggered toward the stove.

"Take my place," Mary said, getting up from her rocking chair. "It's the warmest."

Laura sat stiffly down. She felt numb and stupid. She rubbed her eyes and saw a pink smear on her hand. Her eyelids were bleeding where the snow had scratched them. The sides of the coal heater glowed

355

red-hot and she could feel the heat on her skin, but she was cold inside. The heat from the fire couldn't reach that cold.

Pa sat close to the stove, holding Carrie on his knee. He had taken off her shoes to make sure that her feet were not frozen and he held her wrapped in a shawl. The shawl shivered with Carrie's shivering. "I can't get warm, Pa," she said.

"You girls are chilled through. I'll have you a hot drink in a minute," said Ma, hurrying into the kitchen.

She brought them each a steaming cup of ginger tea.

"My, that smells good!" said Mary and Grace leaning on Laura's knee, looking longingly at the cup till Laura gave her a sip and Pa said, "I don't know why there's not enough of that to go around."

"Maybe there is," said Ma, going into the kitchen again.

It was so wonderful to be there, safe at home, sheltered from the winds and the cold. Laura thought that this must be a little bit like Heaven, where the weary are at rest. She could not imagine that Heaven was better than being where she was, slowly growing warm and comfortable, sipping the hot, sweet, ginger tea, seeing Ma, and Grace, and Pa and Carrie, and Mary all enjoying their own cups of it and hearing the storm that could not touch them here.

"I'm glad you didn't have to come for us, Pa," Laura said drowsily. "I was hoping you were safe."

"So was I," Carrie told Pa, snuggling against him. "I remembered that Christmas, on Plum Creek, when you didn't get home."

"I did, too," Pa said grimly. "When Cap Garland came into Fuller's and said you were all heading out to the open prairie, you can bet I made tracks for a rope and lantern."

"I'm glad we got in all right," Laura woke up to say.

"Yes, we'd have had a posse out looking for you, though we'd have been hunting for a needle in a haystack," said Pa.

"Best forget about it," said Ma.

"Well, he did the best he could," Pa went on. "Cap Garland's a smart boy."

"And now, Laura and Carrie, you're going to bed and get some rest," said Ma. "A good long sleep is what you need."

Focus

1. Laura felt that she was going in the wrong direction, but it was impossible for her to know for sure. Why?
2. How did Laura find Mead's Hotel in the storm?
3. Once they got to Main Street, the trip was only half over. What more did Laura and Carrie have to do?
4. Why do you think that Laura was glad her pa did not have to go out after her?
5. Describe how Laura felt to be home.

357

Nature can be wild and frightening, but it can also be calm and full of wonder. The next story introduces a boy who loves to explore nature. The story is the first chapter of a book called *The Trumpet of the Swan,* which you may want to read someday.

Sam

E. B. WHITE

Walking back to camp through the swamp, Sam wondered whether to tell his father what he had seen.

"I know *one* thing," he said to himself. "I'm going back to that little pond again tomorrow. And I'd like to go alone. If I tell my father what I saw today, he will want to go with me. I'm not sure that's a very good idea."

Sam was eleven. His last name was Beaver. He was strong for his age and had black hair and dark eyes like an Indian. Sam walked like an Indian, too, putting one foot straight in front of the other and making very little noise. The swamp through which he was traveling was a wild place—there was no trail, and it was boggy underfoot, which made walking difficult. Every four or five minutes Sam took his compass out of his pocket

and checked his course to make sure he was headed in a westerly direction. Canada is a big place. Much of it is wilderness. To get lost in the woods and swamps of western Canada would be a serious matter.

As he trudged on, the boy's mind was full of the wonder of what he had seen. Not many people in the world have seen the nest of a Trumpeter Swan. Sam had found one on the lonely pond on this day in spring. He had seen the two great white birds with their long white necks and black bills. Nothing he had ever seen before in all his life had made him feel quite the way he felt, on that wild little pond, in the presence of those two enormous swans. They were so much bigger than any bird he had ever seen before.

The nest was big, too—a mound of

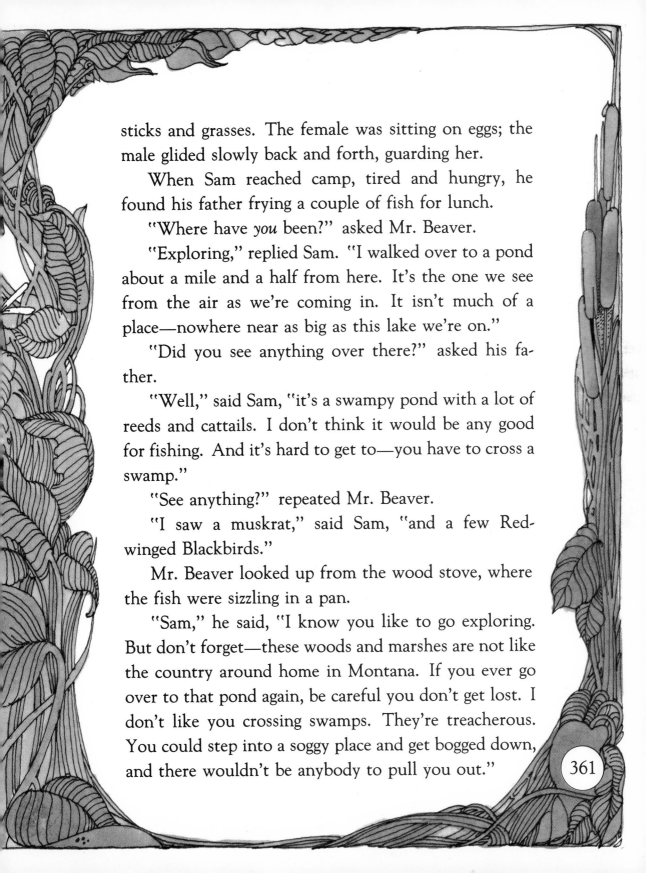

sticks and grasses. The female was sitting on eggs; the male glided slowly back and forth, guarding her.

When Sam reached camp, tired and hungry, he found his father frying a couple of fish for lunch.

"Where have *you* been?" asked Mr. Beaver.

"Exploring," replied Sam. "I walked over to a pond about a mile and a half from here. It's the one we see from the air as we're coming in. It isn't much of a place—nowhere near as big as this lake we're on."

"Did you see anything over there?" asked his father.

"Well," said Sam, "it's a swampy pond with a lot of reeds and cattails. I don't think it would be any good for fishing. And it's hard to get to—you have to cross a swamp."

"See anything?" repeated Mr. Beaver.

"I saw a muskrat," said Sam, "and a few Red-winged Blackbirds."

Mr. Beaver looked up from the wood stove, where the fish were sizzling in a pan.

"Sam," he said, "I know you like to go exploring. But don't forget—these woods and marshes are not like the country around home in Montana. If you ever go over to that pond again, be careful you don't get lost. I don't like you crossing swamps. They're treacherous. You could step into a soggy place and get bogged down, and there wouldn't be anybody to pull you out."

"I'll be careful," said Sam. He knew perfectly well
he would be going back to the pond where the swans
were. And he had no intention of getting lost in the
woods. He felt relieved that he had not told his father
about seeing the swans, but he felt queer about it, too.
Sam was not a sly boy, but he was odd in one respect:
he liked to keep things to himself. And he liked being
alone, particularly when he was in the woods. He enjoyed the life on his father's cattle ranch in the Sweet

Grass country in Montana. He loved his mother. He loved Duke, his cow pony. He loved riding the range. He loved watching the guests who came to board at the Beaver's ranch every summer.

But the thing he enjoyed most in life was these camping trips in Canada with his father. Mrs. Beaver didn't care for the woods, so she seldom went along—it was usually just Sam and Mr. Beaver. They would motor to the border and cross into Canada. There Mr. Beaver would hire a bush pilot to fly them to the lake where his camp was, for a few days of fishing and loafing and exploring. Mr. Beaver did most of the fishing and loafing. Sam did the exploring. And then the pilot would return to take them out. His name was Shorty. They would hear the sound of his motor and run out and wave and watch him glide down onto the lake and taxi his plane in to the dock. These were the pleasantest days of Sam's life, these days in the woods, far, far from everywhere—no automobiles, no roads, no people, no noise, no school, no homework, no problems, except the problem of getting lost. And, of course, the problem of what to be when he grew up. Every boy has *that* problem.

After supper that evening, Sam and his father sat for a while on the porch. Sam was reading a bird book.

"Pop," said Sam, "do you think we'll be coming back to camp again about a month from now—I mean, in about thirty-five days or something like that?"

"I guess so," replied Mr. Beaver. "I certainly hope so. But why thirty-five days? What's so special about thirty-five days?"

"Oh, nothing," said Sam. "I just thought it might be very nice around here in thirty-five days."

"That's the craziest thing I ever heard of," said Mr. Beaver. "It's nice here *all* the time."

Sam went indoors. He knew a lot about birds, and he knew it would take a swan about thirty-five days to hatch her eggs. He hoped he could be at the pond to see the young ones when they came out of the eggs.

Sam kept a diary—a daybook about his life. It was just a cheap notebook that was always by his bed. Every night, before he turned in, he would write in the book. He wrote about things he had done, things he had seen, and thoughts he had had. Sometimes he drew a picture. He always ended by asking himself a question so he would have something to think about while

falling asleep. On the day he found the swan's nest, this is what Sam wrote in his diary:

I saw a pair of trumpeter swans today on a small pond east of camp. The female has a nest with eggs in it. I saw three, but I'm going to put four in the picture—I think she was laying another one. This is the greatest discovery I ever made in my entire life. I did not tell Pop. My bird book says baby swans are called cygnets. I am going back tomorrow to visit the great swans again. I heard a fox bark today. Why does a fox bark? Is it because he is mad, or worried, or hungry, or because he is sending a message to another fox? *Why does a fox bark?*

Sam closed his notebook, undressed, crawled into his bunk and lay there with his eyes closed, wondering why a fox barks. In a few minutes he was asleep.

Focus
1. Where were Sam and his father?
2. Explain what Sam found.
3. What did Mr. Beaver tell Sam to be careful of?
4. Sam liked a lot of things, most of all camping trips with his father. What were some things that the two did on their trips?
5. Why did Sam want to return to the camp in thirty-five days?
6. Tell three things that Sam wrote in his notebook that night.

Sam Beaver recorded his observations in a notebook. Other kinds of records can help us, too. A chart, for example, puts information in order so that you can understand it quickly.

Suppose Sam had just gotten a puppy. He might want to keep a record of its growth. Each week he could record the puppy's weight on the chart. Sam could use this chart to see whether his puppy was gaining weight as it should. Knowing his puppy's weight could help Sam know how much to feed the puppy.

Sometimes directions for feeding puppy food are also in chart form. The feeding chart on the bag of dog food shows that the heavier a puppy gets, the more food it will need to eat.

Look at the two charts on the next page. Notice the titles above each column of numbers. Make sure you understand the abbreviation for pounds (lb.) and the symbol for cup (c). Which chart do you think Sam might have made? Which is the chart that would be shown on the bag of puppy food?

Use the charts to answer the following questions. Write your answers on a sheet of paper.

1. On which chart would you find the number of cups Sam fed the puppy for the first week? How many was it?
2. How many cups did Sam feed the puppy the fifth week? On which chart did you find the answer?
3. How old was Sam's puppy when Sam began feeding him once a day? Where did you find the answer to this question?
4. Puppies often get worms. If they have worms, they lose weight. Use the Weight Chart to tell when Sam's puppy might have had worms. How old was the puppy then?
5. Write a list of ideas for charts that you could make.

WEIGHT CHART	
Puppy's Weight (lbs)	Puppy's Age (Wks)
4 pounds	1 Week
7 pounds	2 Weeks
15 pounds	3 Weeks
21 pounds	4 Weeks
22 pounds	5 Weeks
24 pounds	6 Weeks
25 pounds	7 Weeks
27 pounds	8 Weeks
29 pounds	9 Weeks
32 pounds	10 Weeks
35 pounds	11 Weeks
39 pounds	12 Weeks
41 pounds	13 Weeks
43 pounds	14 Weeks
45 pounds	15 Weeks
47 pounds	16 Weeks
49 pounds	17 Weeks
52 pounds	18 Weeks

COLONEL BOB'S PUPPY CHOW

DIRECTIONS

Puppy's (lbs)	Amount to Feed Per Day (c)
5 or Less	1–2
10–20	3
20–30	5
30–40	7
40–50	8
Over 50	9

Feed your puppy twice each day until it weighs 50 pounds. Then feed once each day.

CHECKPOINT

Vocabulary:
Word
Identification

Read the words listed below. Then choose one word that best completes each sentence. Write the sentences on your paper.

clung   geography   depot
muffler   ginger   particles

1. As they staggered along in the storm the sisters became covered with icy _____ of snow.
2. Laura's _____ book was open in front of her, but she didn't feel like studying.
3. Laura's mother prepared cups of hot _____ tea for the girls.
4. Laura wrapped a warm _____ around Carrie's neck to keep out the cold.

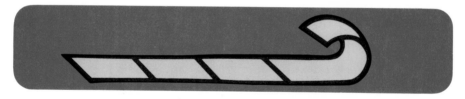

Vocabulary:
Vocabulary
Development
(classification)

Write the headings "Weather Words," "Bad Weather Clothing," and "Things near a Pond" on your paper. Under the correct heading write each word from the following list.

wind   overcoat   swan
blizzard   muskrat   mittens
scarf   snow   reeds

5. Weather Words
6. Bad Weather Clothing
7. Things near a Pond

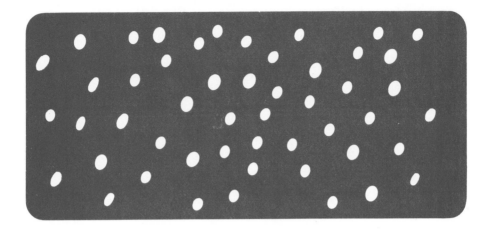

Read the paragraph below and answer the questions that follow.

On Saturday the Bernsteins drove to the beach. They went swimming and then they played badminton. Next Mr. Bernstein got a big basket out of the car. David and Joan laid plates and forks on the table while Mrs. Bernstein started a fire.

8. What will probably happen next?
   a. They will play another game of badminton.
   b. They will lie down for a nap.
   c. They will get dressed and drive home.
   d. They will have a picnic lunch.

José had never seen snow. This was his first winter in snow country. He was waiting impatiently for the first snowstorm. He had heard all about sledding, tobogganing, and making snow castles. Finally, it began to snow. By noontime, there were two feet of snow on the ground.

9. What will probably happen next?
   a. José will sit in front of the fire.
   b. José will decide to watch television.
   c. José will go to play in the snow.
   d. José will start to read his book.

369

Picture Pumpkin

"It's as red as a pumpkin stew," someone said. Now, that is not a common way of describing something. But people often express themselves in unusual ways.

This last group of selections shows people expressing themselves with a pen, a brush, or a story told for all to enjoy. Listen and picture a pumpkin stew.

Poetry is a kind of writing that people use to express themselves. But when Simon and Sarah Smug rely on a special kind of ink for their writing, the results are surprising.

Rhyming Ink

MARGARET BAKER

Once upon a time there was a good man called Simon Smug. His wife was called Sarah, and they kept a shop.

Every morning at eight o'clock precisely, Simon unbolted the shop-door and took down the shutters. Then he stood behind the counter and weighed out sugar and currants and wrapped up parcels and made out bills. To his customers he said, "What next can I get for you, ma'am?" and "Dreadful weather for the time of year!" And every evening as the clock struck seven, Simon put up the shutters again and fastened the door. "Now I'm going to enjoy myself!" he would say, rubbing his hands with satisfaction.

Sometimes he enjoyed himself by sitting with his feet in the fender reading the paper to Sarah. Sometimes he enjoyed himself puttering about the backyard and painting the water-butt or sowing Virginian Stock seed in the rockery. And sometimes he enjoyed himself by just falling asleep in his chair.

Then one day he decided to become a poet.

"You'd be surprised at the thoughts that come into my head, Sarah," said he. "I'm going to put them into

poetry and become famous."

He got a very large sheet of paper and a very large pen and a very large bottle of ink and sat down at the kitchen table. Sarah looked at him proudly.

Simon began to write as fast as he could. "Just listen to this and tell me if you ever heard so fine a beginning to a poem," cried he.

> "Some poets praise the hairy lion;
>
> I praise the hippopotamus. . . ."

"And what comes next?" asked Mrs. Smug.

"I don't know yet," said Simon. "I haven't had time to find a rhyme."

He sat at the table and thought and thought and thought. He bit the end of his pen to shreds, he rumpled his hair and inked his face and made scribbles

and patterns all round the edge of the paper. It was of no use. "I don't believe there's a rhyme to hippopotamus in any language under the sun!" he groaned.

"Why not start with something easier?" suggested Mrs. Smug.

So Simon began again. He began a dozen poems at least, but he could not finish one.

"Is anything wrong, my dear?" asked Sarah.

"Wrong!" echoed Simon, "I should think there is! There's not a single rhyme to any word I've used. I can no more make poetry without rhymes than a bricklayer can make houses without bricks! I'll never be a poet at this rate."

It was the same every time he sat down to write. His verses never got beyond the first two lines, and all for want of rhymes. He then grew quite thin and ill-tempered with worry. He lost his appetite. He lost his sleep. He was impatient with the customers and made mistakes in their orders. Wherever he was and whatever he was doing, he was muttering scraps of poetry to himself and trying to find the words he wanted.

"Things can't go on like this," said Mrs. Smug, but she had not the least idea how to stop them.

375

Then she saw the advertisement for Rhyming Ink. "Important to Poets!" it began; "Here is the Most Wonderful Invention of the Age. Just dip your Pen in Rhyming Ink (Only Ten Shillings a Bottle) and you cannot help writing Poetry. If our Ink fails to find a Rhyme to any Word in the Dictionary, your Money will be refunded."

"Now if that isn't exactly what Simon wants!" she cried, and she sent for some ink immediately. She did not tell Simon anything about it, of course. She felt sure he would not feel like a real poet if he knew his rhymes came out of a bottle instead of out of his head.

When the ink arrived, she washed out the old ink pot that Simon always used and filled it to the brim.

Presently Simon came in, gave a great sigh, and sat down at the kitchen table to write poetry, just as usual. He sighed again as he spread out a clean sheet of paper. He sighed as he chose his pen. He sighed as he opened the ink pot, for he supposed that everything would happen as it had always done before. He felt that in five minutes he would be rumpling his hair and rolling his eyes in his struggles to find a rhyme. He had just thought of such a beautiful beginning for a poem, too!

I would that in the summer sun
I flitted as a butterfly!

He wrote that quite quickly, but that was not surprising because he could always write the first two lines without any trouble at all. The surprising thing was

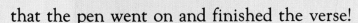

that the pen went on and finished the verse!

> *But then before the day was run,*
> *Perhaps I'd in the gutter lie!*

"I've done it!" shouted Simon Smug. "I've done it! I've written a poem!"

"There now, just fancy that!" said Sarah.

"But I don't suppose I'll ever be able to write another," he added gloomily.

"I should try if I were you," said Sarah.

"I might as well," said Simon. "I'll see if I can finish the hippopotamus one."

He dipped his pen in the ink and began to write:

> *Some poets praise the hairy lion;*
> *I praise the hippopotamus.*

And once again the pen went gliding on:

> *He's got a mouth with teeth like iron—*
> *If he should nip, oh! what a fuss!*

"I've done it again!" he cried. "I can write poetry as easily as signing my name!"

He scrawled "Simon Smug" across the paper by way of illustration and then gave a gasp, for under his name he had written, "Oh, what a mug!"

"I've made a poem even of that," he said in astonishment, "only it's not a very good one. I'm a poet at last! Now I shall sit and write poetry all day long."

"You don't mean it, do you?" asked Mrs. Smug.

"Of course I do," said Simon. "Fancy wasting my time weighing out rice and tea and things like that

377

when I've found out how clever I am! If anyone attends to the shop, it must be you, my dear. I'm going to be far too busy to do anything about it."

At first Mrs. Smug made the best of things, though it was very inconvenient to have to keep running to answer the shop-bell. On the other hand, she was proud to be able to explain to customers that her husband had taken to poetry.

The customers always looked much impressed. "How wonderful!" they said.

It was very pleasant, too, not to have Simon moaning and groaning over his rhymes whenever she came near him. But after a few days she almost wished she had never bought the rhyming ink. The kitchen table was smothered in papers. Poems fluttered to the ground with every opening of the door. Poems got into the wash-tub and the gravy and the flour-barrel and the coal-scuttle. If she had a moment in which to sit down and rest, Simon would begin to read his favorite pieces to her. What with the worry of so much poetry in the kitchen and the worry of so little help in the store, she began to feel quite worn out.

The trouble came to a head when she used the rhyming ink herself. She would never have done it if she had had time to think. The shop was full of customers and she was quite flurried. When she lost her pencil she carried off the ink pot from under Simon's nose.

"But I can't write poetry without ink!" protested Simon.

"Then you can spend the time tidying the kitchen," said Sarah over her shoulder. "It's perfectly disgraceful!"

She wrote receipts and bills and orders and then she took the ink pot back to her husband. Never once did she remember that the ink was not of the ordinary, everyday kind—until the customers returned, red-faced, and angry.

"What do you mean by putting down white mice on my bill?" cried one. "I ordered a pound of rice and you have charged me for three white mice as well."

"And I ordered a pot of jam," said another, "and you've written underneath, 'To boil with ham!'"

"And just look at this receipt!" cried a third. "I never saw a bill receipted like this in my life!"

"Received with thanks,
Dear Mrs. Bankes,
One pound and four—
You owe me more—
A kiss and hug
From Sarah Smug!"

"It's that rhyming ink!" cried poor Sarah. "Nothing's gone right since I bought it!" And she rushed into the kitchen.

"I've written another poem since you've brought me the ink again," said Simon; "it begins,

379

"Behold the wriggling caterpillar!
   That—"

"I don't care how it begins!" cried Mrs. Smug, and she seized the bottle and emptied the ink out of the window all over the rockery. "You'll just clear all those papers off the table and go and look after the shop as you used to do. I've had more than enough poetry.

To tell the truth, Simon had had more than enough poetry, too. He was quite glad to be back behind the counter. But Sarah was wrong when she thought that emptying the bottle out of the window was the end of the matter. The Virginian Stocks began to behave in a most extraordinary way. Instead of being miserable and straggling, they grew and budded and blossomed as though ink was their favorite fertilizer.

"What a charming backyard you have," exclaimed all Simon's visitors; "your rockery is as pretty as a poem!"

Which just shows what rhyming ink can do—at least the kind at ten shillings a bottle.

Focus
1. What did Mr. Smug want to be?
2. How did Mrs. Smug help her husband?
3. Why did Mr. Smug's writing become annoying?
4. What happened when Mrs. Smug used the rhyming ink?
5. Why did Mr. Smug go back to being a shopkeeper?

The Smugs were writers of the make-believe kind. Now you will read about a real writer and a helpful goose.

Will's Quill

Many years ago in Merrie Olde England there lived a country goose named Willoughby Waddle. While the other geese on the farm were content to spend their days nibbling on flowers and floating lazily on the lake, Willoughby was restless. He wanted to see the world. Even more, he wanted to be useful. And so early one spring morning he set out for Londontown.

Once inside the gates of the city, Willoughby was startled to see so many people rushing helter-skelter through the narrow cobblestone streets. It was all he could do to keep from being trampled underfoot or crushed by the wheels of the passing carts and carriages. For a sensitive goose who was used to the quiet countryside, the loud cries of peddlers selling their wares were frightening.

"Come buy my pots and pans!" shouted one crier.

"Ink! Ink!" called out another. "Who will buy my fine writing quills and ink?"

A woman walked by carrying a cage with two scrawny geese trapped inside. When she saw Willoughby she yelled, "Come, my pretty! I can use a plump goose the likes of you!"

Willoughby was terrified—but not so terrified he couldn't escape her grasp. He was beginning to understand why city geese looked so weak and downtrodden. Willoughby hid inside an empty barrel and tried to smooth out his ruffled feathers. If only he could survive this first day in Londontown, he knew he would find some way of being useful.

Just when he felt it was safe for him to venture out again—SWASH! Down from a window came a torrent of dishwater and bits of discarded vegetables. Willoughby was covered from the top of his head to the tip of his tailfeathers! He had just learned that it was common practice for Londoners to empty their dishpans into the streets below.

While he stood there trying to recover from this latest indignity, a bearded young gentleman happened by. He stopped and spoke to Willoughby.

"Allow me to help," he said, brushing the cabbage leaves from Willoughby's wings. "Ah, it does seem as if life is full of trouble, even for a goose."

The gentleman then reached into a leather pouch and brought out a fistful of ripe red berries, which he held in his cupped hand.

"Here, my friend," he said. "Eat."

Never had Willoughby been treated with such kindness. Then and there he vowed that somehow, in some way, he would be of use to this thoughtful man. So when the gentleman quickly walked away, Willoughby did his best to follow. But to his dismay he soon lost sight of his friend. Willoughby found himself standing before the Globe. The Globe was the most famous theater in all London, where every afternoon people came to see plays performed. Could his friend have disappeared into this huge round building? Before he could decide what to do next, he was swept inside the theater by the onrushing crowd of latecomers.

With much effort, Willoughby squeezed in and out between the people's legs. He finally managed to ease his way up to the front near the stage where he could better see the people's faces. The audience was growing more and more excited.

"Ah! Now comes the dueling scene!" said a gentleman standing next to Willoughby. "It is the best part of the play!"

Two men carrying long swords began leaping about, chasing each other around the stage. Willoughby looked up. He recognized the dueler dressed in the bright red costume. It was the very man who had befriended him earlier! Of course, Willoughby didn't know anything about play-acting, and when he saw that his friend was in trouble, he became alarmed. This was his chance to return the favor! Willoughby flew up on the stage and nipped the other dueler by the seat of his breeches.

"Gadzooks!" the man cried. "I've been bit by a wild goose!"

The audience burst into gales of laughter. They hooted and they howled. Then one ruffian shouted, "It is foul play!" which was indeed very rude. The actors tried to go on with their duel, but it was no use. Besides, by now everyone had begun to leave the theater.

When he saw the terrible commotion, Willoughby sensed he had done something wrong. He fled outside as fast as he could. Any other goose would have given up and gone far away, but not Willoughby. He ran and hid behind a tree to wait for his friend. Would he be angry?

When at last the actors came out of the stage door, they seemed in a most jovial mood. Even the two duelers shook hands. "I think that goose was the best part of a bad play," said one of the actors. To this everyone agreed.

"Do write us a good play, Will," pleaded a fellow actor. "We have great need of poetic lines to speak. You are the only writer who sings from the heart."

"I can try," replied the young man called Will. "Tonight I intend to finish the play I have been working on for months. I shall see you later."

Once again Willoughby followed his friend Will. Through one dark street after another they went until Will came to his house. He stepped inside and closed the door after him. For more than an hour Willoughby waited in the moonlit street. Finally, just as he was about to waddle away to find a place to sleep, the shutters of a window opened wide. Willoughby looked up and saw his friend throwing several feathers down into the street.

"These quills!" he was grumbling. "How can I write with such horrible pens?"

Naturally, Willoughby was curious. He went over to inspect the feathers and found that each of their inky tips was badly broken. He immediately knew what was wrong. These pitiful-looking quills had come from city geese! Willoughby stuck his head under his wing and plucked forth one long, strong feather. With his beak he tapped on the door, not once, but many times. At last the door opened.

"Hello, my faithful goose!" Will exclaimed. "What do you wish?" Then, holding up his lantern, he said, "Ah, now I see. You are offering me a quill of your own!"

"It is the answer to my greatest need," he said, lifting Willoughby up in his arms and carrying him to his room. "Come, be my guest."

He gently took the feather from Willoughby's beak and then set about sharpening the quill to a very fine point. Will sat down at his desk and began to write. Willoughby settled happily in a cozy corner and fell into a peaceful sleep.

Throughout the long night the playwright filled one page after another. When the rays of the morning sun beamed through the window, Will stood up and sighed, "It is done!" With a flourish of his new quill he signed his name—

Wm Shakspeare

Then turning to Willoughby, he said, "Without you, dear goose, my play might never have been written."

Willoughby Waddle had indeed become a most useful goose. From that day forward, he and his friend Will made their way to the Globe Theater together, delighting the people of Londontown and filling their hearts with pride.

Focus
1. Why did Willoughby go to London?
2. What trouble and what kindness did Willoughby find in London?
3. How did Willoughby upset the play in the Globe Theater?
4. Who was the man Willoughby helped? Why was the man famous?
5. How did Willoughby help the man?

LIFE SKILL: Telephone Directory

Bookstores today are not like the bookstores of Shakespeare's time. For one thing, bookstores today advertise differently than they did long ago. One place in which modern bookstores advertise is the Yellow Pages.

Each directory page has guide words at the top the way a dictionary does. The guide word on the left tells you the first type of business on that page. The guide word on the right tells you the last type of business on that page.

Look at the sample directory on the next page. Notice the headings in large, dark type. They tell the kinds of businesses you will find on the page. For example, to find a list of bookstores you would look under the heading "Book Dealers—Retail."

The listings under each heading give you the names, addresses, and phone numbers of businesses described in the heading. Some businesses also have advertisements on the page.

Study the sample directory page and answer the following questions. Write your answers on a sheet of paper.

1. How can you quickly tell what is listed on the directory page?
2. What are the boxes on a directory page for?
3. Suppose your class wants to print a book of stories. So you look up "Book Printers." What would you do next?
4. Suppose you want to buy a book for a child. Which bookstores would you call? Why?
5. Your friends love to sail. Which bookstores would be likely to have a book they would enjoy?

Boats—Books

Boat Trailers
See Trailer Renting & Leasing:
Trailers—Boat

Boat Yards
Stewart's Marina
   Indian Ave. Oldport 555-9777

Bologna
See Meat—Meat Packers; Sausages;
Wholesale

Bolts
Aqua Knack Fasteners
   8 East Rd. Warren 555-2324
Rentco, Inc.
   50 Master Ave. Oldport 555-8900

Bonds—Investment
See Stock & Bond Brokers

Bonds—Surety & Fidelity
Crayman Packer Agency
   34 Short Wharf Oldport 555-7800
Curt, Inc.
   Goodview Terr. Oldport 555-9100
Midville Ins. Agency
   West Ave. Oldport 555-7868

Book Dealers—Retail
The Best Books
A Complete Bookstore
Special Children's Section
Lending Library
We Mail & Special Order
Credit Cards Accepted
Best Books
Market St. Oldport 555-7200

Chase & Find Books
   "The Search Ends Here"
   59 Water St. Oldport 555-9822
Family Bookstore
   100 Narrow St. Oldport 555-8765
Harriet's Book Shop
Harvey Community Books
   505 East Ave. Sleepdale 555-8900
Sailors' Salon Bookstore
   Plaza Lane Oldport 555-1100
Sarah's Bookshop, Inc.
   44 Green St. Warren 555-0700
University Bookstore
   Base St. Oldport 555-4433

Book Dealers—Used & Rare
Collections & Libraries Purchased
Out of Print Titles Searched
   50 Lincoln St. Oldport 555-1100
Brattle Bookstore
   4 East St. Beantown 555-4299
Connor's Book Shop
   400 Summer St. Oldport 555-3232
Courant Company, The
   13 Wise St. Warren 555-4321
Lawrence Book Shop
   50 Post Rd. Diverton 555-0070

Book Printers
See Printers

Book Publishers
See Publishers—Books

Bookbinders
Anne's Bindery Service
   44 High St. Oldport 555-9040
Cardwell Bindings
   56 Lincoln St. Oldport 555-7676

389

Willoughby Waddle is a made-up goose. His story is made-up, too. But William Shakespeare was a real person. Many of his plays were performed in the Globe Theater.

SHAKESPEARE'S GLOBE THEATER

DIANA TOUSLEY BLAZAR

Will Shakespeare wasn't always a playwright. At first he wanted to be an actor. He wanted to get into the make-believe world of the stage and perform for audiences. So when he was 22, Will left his home in Stratford and headed for the great theaters of London.

Londoners loved going to see plays. During the time that Shakespeare lived in London, plays were as popular as movies are today. People would come from miles around to spend a few hours in the theater.

The greatest theater of London was the Globe. This is where Will Shakespeare's plays were first performed. Today the Globe is almost as famous as Shakespeare himself.

The Globe was specially built for London audiences. The stage was a platform built on the ground. The space in front of the stage was called the "pit." Farmers from around London could come into town and, for a penny, stand in the pit close to the actors. To the sides of the stage were seats. Merchants could pay a few pennies and sit in them. Behind the pit and to the sides above the seats were the galleries. The galleries were special places with comfortable chairs. A seat in the galleries might cost as much as twelve pennies.

To understand what the Globe was like you have to remember that there was no electricity in those days. Plays were performed in the daytime. The theater had to be built to let in light. So there was no roof over the stage. The pit and the stage were open to the sky.

There was no curtain in front of the stage and almost no scenery on it. The actors had to make the plays seem real by their words and movements. The audience had to be told what the scenes were. Children would walk across the stage carrying signs. The signs

would say, "Woods," or "Forest," or "Town." The actors could wear colorful costumes, but they had to rely on their skill to entertain the audience. The audiences would get involved, too. When a villain was sneaking up on a hero, the people would shout, "Look behind you! Watch out!"

At the back of the stage was the upper stage. The upper stage was used as an extra room, like a bedroom in a house. Above the upper stage sat the musicians.

Besides musicians there were trumpeters. The trumpeters might be part of a play, but their main job was to announce the beginning of a performance. Three loud blasts would signal the start of a play.

The loud blasts of the trumpets were not the only loud noises in the Globe. The people were noisy too. Going to the theatre was like going to a carnival. Some people would bring food. Others would buy meat turnovers or pies from vendors in the theater. Everyone talked at once. When the trumpets sounded, everyone would cheer and then wait for the play to begin.

A special treat for the audience would be to see Will Shakespeare act in a play. But most of the time Will would stand to the side of the stage. There he would direct the actors. The audiences loved Will and his plays, and they loved their Globe Theater.

Focus

1. Describe the Globe Theater. Give three details.
2. Why was the roof of the theater open to the sun?
3. Describe what the audience was like before a play. Give three examples.
4. What did Will Shakespeare do at the Globe Theater?
5. How did Londoners feel about the Globe Theater?

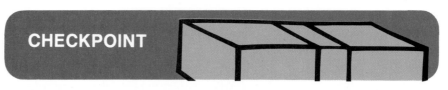

CHECKPOINT

Vocabulary:
Word
Identification

Below are ten new words followed by six questions. Answer each question using a word from the list.

flourish   rely   astonished   parcels
extraordinary   ventured   involved   vowed

1. What is another word for *packages*?
2. What would you be if you were amazed?
3. Which word describes a fancy decoration?
4. Which word means "special"?
5. Which word is a synonym for *depend*?
6. What is another word for *promised*?

Comprehension:
Referents

Read the following paragraph. Think about who or what the underlined words stand for. On your paper write the answer to each question.

Willoughby followed Will to the theater. He watched Will and another actor dueling on the stage. When Willoughby thought Will was in trouble, the goose rushed through the audience and onto the stage. The goose wanted to help *his friend.*

7. What do the words *his friend* stand for?
  a. another actor   b. Willoughby   c. Will
  d. the audience

Simon Smug could not make his poetry rhyme. So his wife bought him some rhyming ink. Every time Simon dipped his pen into <u>it</u> and began to write, he filled his paper with rhymes.

8. What does the underlined *it* stand for?

   a. pen   b. paper   c. ink   d. poetry

Read the sentences below. On your paper write the correct meaning for each of the underlined words.

Decoding: Suffixes *-ant, -ance*

9. Willoughby watched the <u>performance</u> of the play.

   a. one who performs   c. perform again

   b. capable of performing   d. the act of performing

10. Simon Smug needed some <u>assistance</u> in rhyming his poems.

   a. the act of assisting   c. able to assist

   b. one who assists   d. not assisting

Printers
Alpha Printing
   Apple St., Redville 555–0408
Fable Printing Press
   Story Rd., Greentown 555–6849

Radio Systems
Redville Communications, Inc.
   Green Rd., Redville 555–2024

Railroads—Model
A—Z Hobby Shop
   Play St., Greentown 555–1302

Reading Improvement
Rapid Reading Clinic
   Berton Lane, Redville 555–1188
Ready Reading Co.
   School St., Greentown 555–6400

Use the sample Telephone Directory to answer the following questions.

Life Skill: Resources (telephone directory)

12. Blanca wants to buy some track for her model railroad. Which telephone number should she dial?

13. If you lived in Greentown and wanted something printed, which store would you call?

14. What is the telephone number of the Rapid Reading Clinic?

A thankful young fellow named Fred
Said, "My favorite color is red.
    I'm one lucky fellow
    It might have been yellow—
And I hate yellow!" That's what he said.

Q. Why did the elephant
guard the haystack?
A. He was watching his diet.

Knock! knock!
Who's there?
Gwynne.
Gwynne who?
Gwynne the house and stay there!

New Book
Saddle Sores
   by Rhoda Bronco

Double Bunk
"Why don't you take the top bunk for a change?"
"No, I don't want to oversleep."

You don't need a theater full of people to tell a bad joke. Just follow Scott Corbett's advice and try your bad jokes on your friends.

So You Want to Write Bad Jokes!

SCOTT CORBETT

This letter will do one of two things for you. Either it will teach you to write bad jokes, or prove you can't. Don't think learning how will be easy. Writing bad jokes is no laughing matter. If you read these jokes and still haven't learned anything, then take up bird-watching instead of bad joke writing. It's better for you anyway, because it gets you out into the fresh air.

Anatomy Lesson
Each part of our body, it's easy to show,
Has its own special job, from our brains to our heart,
But what about our middle toe?
What is its function, what is its art?
Well, it's very important, I'll have you know:
It keeps our other toes apart.

Q. What's a bow tie?
A. Two winners in an
   archery contest.

New Book
Baker's Man
      by Pat E. Cake
New Book
Be Prepared!
      by Justin Case

Most bad jokes are written in stuffy rooms.

The best way to write bad jokes is with a pencil, so that you can erase them. Jokes are hard to write, so use a hard lead pencil. Write them in a secret code if you can, and try to disguise your handwriting.

There are many types of BJs, but we will mention only a few here. One of the worst types of BJs is the "is-so" joke:

My grandpa is so strong he can pitch horseshoes without taking them off the horse.

Q. Why does an elephant rub vanishing
cream on his body?
A. It helps an elephant hide.

Q. How can you make
an elephant laugh?
A. Tell him a rhinocerous joke.

    Any BJ writer would be pretty proud of that one,
and you, too, can write jokes that bad if you try. All it
takes is practice and lots of nerve.

    One of the oldest BJs we have is the riddle:

Q. How can you tell how much a tapeworm eats?
A. Buy him a tape recorder.

Another common type of BJ is the knock-knock:

Knock! knock!

Who's there?

Upton.

Upton who?

Upton no good.

Elephant jokes are also very big in the BJ field.
What did elephants ever do to deserve these? Nobody
tells hyena jokes, but hyenas laugh at elephant jokes
and everything else.

Short Story
Once upon a time, five seconds ago,
I started this poem with a capital O.
In another five seconds, as you will see,
I am going to end it with a capital Z.

Even elephant jokes and knock-knocks, however,
are harmless compared to limericks. Where limericks
are concerned, here's a word of warning:
    If it's limericks you're longing to write,
    Then you're in a deplorable plight;
        If you read them aloud
        To your neighborhood crowd,
    They all move away in the night.
    Once you're caught in the limerick's grip,
    It's worse than the plague or the pip;
        In writing, we're told,
        The limericks hold
    The featherweight championship.
    And never read more than ten pages of BJs at one
sitting, or even one standing. Think of your health!
Signed,

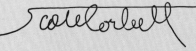

Knock! knock!
Who's there?
Sawyer.
Sawyer who?
Sawyer picture
in the paper.

Knock! knock!
Who's there?
Knock.
Knock who?
Knock it off, we've
had enough!

Focus

1. What are the five types of bad jokes that Scott Corbett describes?
2. Why shouldn't you read more than ten pages of BJs at a time?
3. Which of the jokes do you like best? Which do you like the least? Tell why.
4. Write a BJ of your own. Tell what kind it is.

401

Scott Corbett wrote about one kind of humor, the joke. Jim Bridger is funny, too, but in a different way.

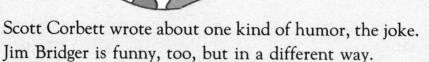

Jim Bridger's
Alarm Clock SID FLEISCHMAN

Jim Bridger was a mighty tall man. When he stubbed his big toe, it took six minutes before he felt it and yelled "Ouch." But he's not famous for being tall.

Jim Bridger was a long-haired mountain man. In fringed buckskins and Indian moccasins, he wandered through the wilderness of the Old West before almost anyone else. It was Jim who brushed the hair out of his eyes and first discovered the Great Salt Lake. They might have named it after him but no one believed he'd found water you couldn't sink in. Jim shrugged his big, bony shoulders and headed back to the mountains.

One day his horse broke three front teeth grazing on a patch of green grass. That's how Jim discovered a petrified forest. The grass and trees had turned to stone for miles around. "Petrified, all petrified," he reported when he got back to civilization. "The bees and the wild flowers, and yes sir, some of those trees had petrified birds on their limbs, singing petrified songs."

But he's not famous for all those things.

Jim Bridger was a ramshackle, sharp-eyed army

scout. In time they named a fort and a forest after him, and a pass and a creek and a mountain or two.

One day while talking to a stranger, Jim pointed to a mountain in the distance. It was flat-topped and red as a Navajo blanket. "Stranger," he said. Jim liked to talk to strangers; they were so few and far between in the wilderness. "Stranger, look how that mountain has grown! When I first came out here, it was nothing but a red anthill."

And that's what Jim Bridger is famous for. That mountain. He made an alarm clock out of it.

The way it happened was this. Jim was out in the wilderness, as usual, when a blizzard whipped down out of Canada. His beard froze. The fringe in his buckskins froze, and his long hair hung like icicles. Then a spark

from his campfire lit inside his moccasin. That spark was so cold it frostbit him, and Jim decided it was time to find himself a warmer climate. He headed south.

Jim traveled through the snow for days and nights. He didn't dare to stop and rest. He knew a man could sleep himself to death in the blizzard and bitter cold.

After a time Jim was all tuckered out and knew he couldn't go much further. Then, through the chill daylight, he caught sight of that red, flat-topped mountain in the distance. It was slab-sided, too, and he had bounced echoes off it many a time. He reckoned that from where he now stood, it would take about eight hours for an echo to return.

So Jim Bridger gave a yip of joy and made camp. He laid out his bedroll on the snow. Then he gave an ear-quivering yell:

"WAKE UP! WAKE UP, JIM BRIDGER, YOU FROSTBIT, NO-ACCOUNT RASCAL!"

Then he climbed into his bedroll, clamped his eyes shut, and started snoring. Oh, he snored thunderbolts, and dreamed of hot biscuits and gravy.

Exactly seven hours and fifty-six minutes later, Jim Bridger's Alarm Clock went off.

"Wake up!" roared the echo. "Wake up, Jim Bridger, you frostbit, no-account rascal!"

Jim roused from his bedroll, all refreshed and feeling strong as a new rope. It was a week before he reached Fort Bridger, where the sun was shining and no one believed his story.

But a trapper came straggling in and said, "It's true, every word. I found the coals of Jim's campfire, and I bundled up in furs to catch some shuteye. Next thing I knew, that mountain commenced booming. I didn't get a wink of sleep. Blast it, Jim, you snore loud enough to drive pigs to market!"

Focus

1. Explain how Jim Bridger's alarm clock worked.
2. To exaggerate means to say that something is larger or more than it really is. Give two examples of Jim Bridger's exaggerating.
3. When Jim told his story at Fort Bridger, no one believed it. What happened to make the people at Fort Bridger change their minds?

You've met Jim Bridger. Now meet the person who wrote about that famous frontiersman as Lee Richmond interviews Sid Fleischman.

Interview with Sid Fleischman

LEE RICHMOND

Lee Richmond: Where'd you get the idea for "Jim Bridger's Alarm Clock?"
Sid Fleischman: That's a book I'd been wanting to write for years. Jim Bridger was a favorite quirky Western character of mine. I had read a children's book on the life of Jim Bridger, and nowhere did the author mention Jim Bridger's famous sense of humor. I couldn't imagine writing about Jim Bridger without mentioning his sense of humor. So I decided to write my own version of Jim Bridger's story. I loved his echo . . . the alarm clock . . . the echo mountain.

L.R.: So the alarm clock story came from Jim Bridger himself?
S.F.: Yes. But Jim Bridger didn't know how to write. All of the tall tales we have of his are from other people who claim to have heard him. So there are different versions, and the language is different for each one.

407

L.R.: So that means Jim Bridger was a real person.

S.F.: Oh, absolutely! Yes, the things in the story about him are true. He did stumble across the Great Salt Lake, and he was a trailblazer. There are mountains named after him in Wyoming, and he was one of the first people to go up into Yellowstone. Yes, he was a trailblazer. That's all quite accurate.

L.R.: How did he live, then, all alone out there in the middle of the wilderness?

S.F.: Well, he was a trapper, and he became a guide for the army. He knew the mountains backwards and forwards. He wasn't really alone. He took people out into the wilderness. That's how the storytelling started. In the evenings, sitting around the fire, he'd tell his tall tales.

L.R.: That's fascinating. How'd you find out about him? How'd you find out about all this?

S.F.: I did a lot of reading about the West. I kept coming across Jim Bridger's name. He was important to the opening of the West. These tales of his amused me. I'd say twelve or fourteen years passed before I finally wrote "Jim Bridger's Alarm Clock."

L.R.: You mentioned tall tales. Was Jim Bridger the one who had the idea of tall tales, or have they been around before?

S.F.: The tall tale is a very old form. It's in almost all folklore . . . and very often different countries have the same tales. When the tall tale got to the American frontier it fell on very fertile soil. People living on the frontier had very little, and so they needed to brag about something. They would brag about how awful the weather was, or how fast the crops would grow, or how big the mosquitoes were. But no, the tall tale is very old. Let me say something about the tall tale, a feeling of mine.

L.R.: Sure, go on.
S.F.: Tall tales tell stories without sticking to the truth. And tall tales are always told with a straight face as if they were the absolute truth. The teller always supports the story with all kinds of real bits of truth to make it more—

L.R.: To see what he can get away with?
S.F.: Yes, but it's . . . it's like being a magician, which I used to be.

L.R.: Oh! What was it like, being a magician? What was that all about?
S.F.: Well, that was fascinating. I was very young. I traveled with a magic show for a couple of years. The show traveled throughout the Middle West. We played one-night stands in just about every small town in the

Midwest. I loved it. I used to invent magic tricks. I loved performing. I still keep up with magic. Little bits of magic turn up in my books. And of course, I've written a book for children on a magician, *Mr. Mysterious and Company*. I also did a book for children on magic tricks that they could do.

L.R.: Do you think there's a similarity between magic and writing?

S.F.: There's a great similarity. Of course, a magician presents something and fools you. He doesn't tell you how it's done—which is the only difference. In a book, the writer is, in a sense, fooling you, because you don't know what's going to happen next. You don't find out how the trick is done, or how the story is done, until the very end. This is particularly true of a mystery story. I find a great similarity between magic and writing.

L.R.: Ah, how did you learn to write?

S.F.: Most writers are self-taught—as are most magicians. I began in high school. I wrote a book of original magic tricks, which was published. I was seventeen. The book is still in print.

L.R.: Good for you!

S.F.: I sold the book outright for fifty dollars. Then I wrote five more books for magicians, but I soon realized that I couldn't write magic forever.

L.R.: What did you do then?

S.F.: I became interested in short stories and that's how it started. I kept on writing more and more. Writing is a game of patience and self-confidence. You just never know when you're going to turn that corner and become professional. It can be the third story that does it, or it might be the thirtieth story. But nothing is wasted.

L.R.: What kind of advice do you have for children who want to start writing stories?

S.F.: The most important thing is to read and develop language, because one deals with language in writing. Then simply try writing stories, and realize that one has to practice storywriting. If you're going to play baseball, you have to practice catching a ball and hitting a ball. If you're getting music lessons, why, that takes practice, too. Writing is no different. It takes a lot of practice. I know that lots of students want to write. When I visit schools children show me their stories. They want to know what publishers to send them to. I tell them to send their stories to their favorite publishers. But let's see, you want specific advice? Practice.

L.R.: That's fine. Where do you get the ideas for your stories?

S.F.: That's another question that children often ask. It's not so hard to find an idea. The ideas are all over. Ideas come from history or things that you see around you. The real problem is knowing what to do with the story. You need to know how to develop a story after you get the idea—that's really where the work comes in. The ideas are simply all over.

L.R.: Do your ideas start with a character, or a theme, or a setting?

S.F.: Of course they're all slightly different. I usually

start with a background—something that excites me, whether it's the gold rush, or pirates, or the West, or something like that. Then I try to imagine what certain characters would be like in that background.

L.R.: Are your stories always funny?
S.F.: I always start out to write very serious books, and something happens somewhere. About the second paragraph I can't resist the comic line. Before I know it, I'm exaggerating all over the place, and laughing out loud at the typewriter. I start out to write serious books, but they always turn out to be comic. I had a color-blind uncle. He lived in Palm Springs. He took up painting. I don't know how he did it. He always painted the desert. I asked him once, "Why do you always paint the desert?" and he said that very often he started out to paint something else, but it always turned out to look like the desert! *(laughter)*

L.R.: Your stories sound like somebody talking. Is that the way you like to write?
S.F.: Yes. I'm very much interested in folk language, particularly American folk language. I love the imagery, and the marvelous phrases that different people use. I just came across a phrase the other day. Someone said that something was as red as a stewed pumpkin. A stewed pumpkin wouldn't occur to me.

L.R.: Do you also draw the pictures for your books?

S.F.: No. No, I don't. There are artists that I'm very fond of. I wish I were an artist, but I'm not. Students ask, "Do you tell the artist what to draw?" I don't. I feel as though I wouldn't want the artist telling me how to write the book, and I don't feel that I should tell the artist how to illustrate it.

L.R.: So the artist, then, decided how Jim Bridger looked.

S.F.: That's right. The only thing I asked for in that book was that the mountain be a kind of Navajo red. That was the only request I made.

L.R.: You felt strongly about the mountain.

S.F.: Yes, I did.

L.R.: Well, Mr. Fleischman, this has been a fine interview. I hope that you'll entertain us with many more books in the future.

Focus

1. Who is Sid Fleischman?
2. Why did Mr. Fleischman write about Jim Bridger?
3. Mr. Fleischman gave some facts about Jim Bridger. Tell three facts.
4. How does Mr. Fleischman get ideas for his stories?
5. What advice does Mr. Fleischman give readers?

Suppose you have to write a report about your city or town. You have already looked at all the books, magazines, and newspapers you could find. Where else could you look for information?

An interview is a good way to get first-hand information. By talking with someone, you may learn things you could not learn from a printed page.

The first step in doing an interview is to ask the person for an appointment. Be sure to tell the person why you want the interview. If you want to use a tape recorder, ask permission. Be ready to take notes.

When you interview someone, you should ask good questions. Learn as much about your subject as you can before you begin your interview. For example, if you are interviewing an author, you may want to read the author's books. How can you tell that Lee Richmond read Sid Fleischman's story about Jim Bridger?

Make a list of questions beforehand. Try to ask questions that give you more than a *yes* or *no* answer. Questions that begin with the words *who, what, when, where, how,* and *why* will get you more information than questions that can be answered with *yes* or *no.* Be ready to think of new questions during the interview if they seem to be needed.

Remember the purpose of the interview. If you are doing a report on your city and decide to interview your grandfather, ask such questions as:

1. How did you get from place to place when you were my age?
2. What was your elementary school like?
3. What has changed since you were nine?

Let the person you are interviewing do most of the talking. Your purpose is to learn the person's ideas, not to hear your own ideas.

Make sure you have all the information you need before you end the interview. Then thank the person for helping you.

When you have finished your report, you may wish to give a copy to the person you interviewed.

Follow these suggestions for interviewing:

1. Set up an appointment.
2. Write your questions ahead of time.
3. Take notes on the answers given to you.
4. Thank the person for helping you.

Now, on a separate piece of paper, answer the following questions.

1. Make a list of subjects you are interested in. Who would you want to interview to find out about these subjects?
2. How would you set up an interview?
3. What kinds of questions are best for interviews? Give a few examples.
4. Why should you make a list of questions before the interview?
5. Suppose you are going to write a story about a circus elephant. What would you ask the elephant trainer in an interview?

Sid Fleischman writes books. Rosa Bonheur paints pictures. What do you think they have in common?

ROSA BONHEUR

CONSTANCE MCALLISTER

Rosa pushed her hair behind her ears and squinted her dark brown eyes. She wanted to examine the picture she had painted for her father. It wasn't as good as she would have liked, but it would have to do, she thought. After all, she was only six years old. The picture was her very best work. She climbed down off her chair and ran into the next room where her mother sat writing a letter.

"Mama, please."

Mrs. Bonheur put down the pen and turned to her lively little daughter.

"I have a picture for Papa," Rosa said. "Will you send it to him with your letter?"

"So you are a little artist now," her mother said with a smile. "You are just like your Papa." She smoothed Rosa's silky brown hair.

Both mother and daughter felt a little sad when they thought about Mr. Bonheur. He was far away in

Paris. But soon Mr. Bonheur would find an apartment for them and the family would be together again.

Rosa's brothers, four-year-old Auguste, and baby Isidore, were playing on the floor. They were too young to understand that the family would soon be moving.

But Rosa knew, and she was filled with questions about the move. "When will we go? Where will we live? Will we have a nice house like this one? Will we have a garden and fields to play in? Will there be room for all our pets?"

Mrs. Bonheur folded the letter and addressed it to her husband in care of some friends in Paris. With the letter she enclosed the picture that Rosa had made for her Papa.

"We will have to wait and see, little one. But we will find a way for you to have some of the pets you love. Soon we will all be together again."

Her mother's words made Rosa happy. "Come, Auguste," she called to her little brother. "Let's pretend we are horses and trot around the garden."

A year later, in April 1829, the family was reunited in Paris. They moved into an apartment on the Rue St. Antoine. There Mr. Bonheur painted in his studio room, when he wasn't out giving art lessons. All the children loved to watch him and to try making pictures of their own. They especially liked to draw animals, and they kept many pets. They loved animals and used them as models for their pictures. Rosa, Auguste, and Isidore all grew up to be artists and became better-known than their father.

In 1830 another baby daughter was born to the Bonheurs. They named her Juliette, but Rosa called her Juju. She was to become a painter, too. But of all the Bonheurs, Rosa would be the most successful. Maybe that was because she worked so hard.

When Rosa was eleven years old, her mother died. Mr. Bonheur could not take care of the children himself. Little Juliette was sent to live with friends in Bordeaux. Auguste and Isidore went away to boarding school. But what was to be done about Rosa?

Papa Bonheur worked out a plan. Each morning he would give Rosa an assignment for the day. Sometimes he made a still-life arrangement for her to paint: Other times he would set out a statue for her to draw. In the evening he would look through her pictures and show her how they could be improved. Soon Rosa was skillful enough to copy paintings. She would spend whole days in the famous Paris museum, the Louvre. There she would copy one or another of the paintings. Some of her pictures were good enough to be sold. Rosa was pleased to be able to add to the family's income.

But what Rosa liked most of all was to be off in the woods or the parks. She loved sketching animals in their natural settings.

When she couldn't be outdoors, Rosa painted the

pets she kept at home. The Bonheurs had a large studio. Now they had plenty of room for their easels and supplies. At one end was a sort of closet that they fitted up as a stall for larger animals such as goats and lambs. There were six flights of stairs down to the ground floor. When the animals were taken out for a romp, the goat would walk downstairs. The lambs had to be carried.

Whenever she could, Rosa would go to fairs. There she could see and sketch large numbers of animals.

In 1853 Rosa Bonheur finished perhaps her best-known painting, *The Horse Fair*. This was an enormous picture. It was eight feet high and more than sixteen feet long. In order to work on the top part of the picture she had to climb a ladder.

In the 1800s women wore dresses with skirts that reached to the ground. Rosa Bonheur found that in such clothes she could not do all the things she wanted to do. So she tried wearing slacks and a blue smock for painting. She liked the outfit so well that she wore it often even though other people found it shocking.

As soon as she had earned enough money to buy a home of her own, Rosa Bonheur moved to the village of By. From her home there she could walk through a gate in her yard right into the woods across the road. The forest was filled with wild animals then. In the forest Rosa could study rabbits, squirrels, wild boars, and deer in their natural surroundings.

She also kept many pets at home. She had dogs, monkeys, parrots, horses, sheep, and goats—even a pair of lions! "To be loved by wild animals," she said, "you must love them." The love that Rosa Bonheur felt for all the animals she painted can be seen in her pictures. Her love for animals is the quality that makes her work special.

Focus

1. What was Rosa's childhood like? Give three details.
2. How did Rosa Bonheur become famous?
3. How can you tell from the story that Rosa loved animals?
4. How is Rosa Bonheur like Sid Fleischman?

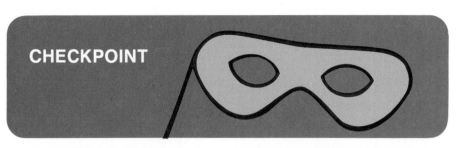

CHECKPOINT

Vocabulary:
Word
Identification

Read the words listed below. You have read these words in the stories of this unit. Write the words on your paper. Next to each word write its definition.

1. fringed   artist's workroom
2. disguise   wild pig
3. studio   began
4. commenced   bad situation
5. plight   trimmed with bunched threads
6. boar   change to look like something else

Vocabulary:
Vocabulary
Development
(context clues)

Sometimes you can figure out the meaning of new words from clues in the sentence. Read the sentences below. Write each sentence on your paper. Replace the underlined word with a synonym from below.

7. Jim Bridger told fantastic stories. He liked to <u>amplify</u> the truth of the tales he told.

    exaggerate   soften   relate

8. Sid Fleischman uses <u>reference</u> books to learn about the subjects he is interested in.

    inexpensive   informational   foreign

There are many different types of jokes. They are alike in some ways and different in others. Read the paragraph about jokes below. On your paper write the answer to each question.

The "is-so" joke, the elephant joke, and the limerick are types of bad jokes. The elephant joke asks a question and must be about elephants. Limericks and "is-so" jokes do not ask questions. Limericks are in the form of a rhyming poem. The "is-so" joke is a statement. Limericks and "is-so" jokes are usually about people. Each kind of joke has its own special form.

9. How are "is-so" jokes, elephant jokes, and limericks alike?
   a. They all ask questions.
   b. They are all jokes.
   c. They are all poems.
   d. They are all about people.
10. How are they different from each other?
   a. They all ask different questions.
   b. They are all written in different forms.
   c. They all rhyme in different ways.
   d. They are all about different people.

THE BLUE MOOSE

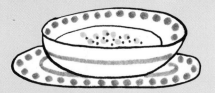

by Manus Pinkwater

Moose Meeting

Mr. Breton had a little restaurant on the edge of the big woods. There was nothing north of Mr. Breton's house except nothing, with trees in between. When winter came, the north wind blew through the trees and froze everything solid. Then it would snow. Mr. Breton didn't like it.

Mr. Breton was a very good cook. Every day, people from the town came to his restaurant. They ate gallons of his special clam chowder. They ate plates of his special beef stew. They ate fish stew and Mr. Breton's special homemade bread. The people from the town never talked much and they never said anything about his cooking.

"Did you like your clam chowder?" Mr. Breton would ask.

"Yup," the people from the town would say.

429

Mr. Breton wished they would say, "Delicious!" or, "Good chowder, Breton!" All they ever said was, "yup." In winter they came on skis and snowshoes.

Every morning Mr. Breton went out behind his house to get firewood. He wore three sweaters, a scarf, galoshes, a woolen hat, a big checkered coat, and mittens. He still felt cold. Sometimes animals came out of the woods to watch Mr. Breton. Raccoons and rabbits came. The cold didn't bother them. It bothered Mr. Breton even more when they watched him.

One morning there was a moose in Mr. Breton's yard. It was a blue moose. When Mr. Breton went out his back door, the moose was there, looking at him. After a while, Mr. Breton went back in, closed the door, and made a pot of coffee while he waited for the moose to go away. It didn't go away; it just stood in Mr. Breton's yard, looking at his back door. Mr. Breton drank a cup of coffee. The moose stood in the yard. Mr. Breton opened the door again. "Shoo! Go away!" he said.

"Do you mind if I come in and get warm?" the moose said. "I'm just about frozen." The moose brushed past him and walked into the kitchen. His antlers almost touched the ceiling.

The moose sat down on the floor next to Mr. Breton's stove. He closed his eyes and sat leaning toward the stove for a long time. Mr. Breton stood in the kitchen, looking at the moose. The moose didn't move. Wisps of steam began to rise from his blue fur. After a long time the moose sighed. It sounded like a foghorn.

"Can I get you a cup of coffee?" Mr. Breton asked the moose. "Or some clam chowder?"

"Clam chowder," said the moose.

Mr. Breton filled a bowl with creamy clam chowder and set it on the floor. The moose dipped his big nose into the bowl and snuffled up the chowder. He made a sort of slurping, whistling noise.

"Sir," the moose said, "this is wonderful clam chowder."

Mr. Breton blushed a very deep red. "Do you really mean that?"

"Sir," the moose said, "I have eaten some very good chowder in my time, and yours is the very best."

"Oh my," said Mr. Breton, blushing even redder. "Oh my. Would you like some more?"

"Yes, with crackers," said the moose.

The moose ate seventeen bowls of chowder with crackers. Then he had twelve pieces of hot gingerbread and forty-eight cups of coffee. While the moose slurped and whistled, Mr. Breton sat in a chair. Every now and then he said to himself, "Oh my. The best he's ever eaten. Oh my."

Later, when some people from the town came to Mr. Breton's house, the moose met them at the door. "How many in your party, please?" the moose asked.

431

"I have a table for you; please follow me."

The people from the town were surprised to see the moose. They felt like running away, but they were too surprised. The moose led them to a table, brought them menus, looked at each person, snorted, and clumped into the kitchen.

"There are some people outside; I'll take care of them," he told Mr. Breton.

The people were whispering to one another about the moose, when he clumped back to the table.

"Are you ready to order?"

"Yup," the people from the town said. They waited for the moose to ask them if they would like some chowder, the way Mr. Breton always did. But the moose just stared at them as though they were very foolish. The people felt uncomfortable. "We'll have the clam chowder."

"Chaudière de Clam; very good," the moose said. "Do you desire crackers or homemade bread?"

"We will have crackers," said the people from the town.

"I suggest you have the bread; it is hot," said the moose.

"We will have bread," said the people from the town.

"And for dessert," said the moose, "will you have fresh gingerbread or Apple Jacquette?"

"What do you recommend?" asked the people from

the town.

"After the Chaudière de Clam, the gingerbread is best."

"Thank you," said the people from the town.

"It is my pleasure to serve you," said the moose. The moose brought bowls of chowder balanced on his antlers.

At the end of the meal, the moose clumped to the table. "Has everything been to your satisfaction?" he asked.

"Yup," said the people from the town, their mouths full of gingerbread.

"I beg your pardon?" said the moose. "What did you say?"

"It was very good," said the people from the town. "It was the best we've ever eaten."

"I will tell the chef," said the moose.

The moose clumped into the kitchen and told Mr. Breton that the people from the town had said that the food was the best they had ever eaten. Mr. Breton rushed out of the kitchen and out of the house. The people from the town were sitting on the porch, putting on their snowshoes.

"Did you tell the moose that my clam chowder was the best you've ever eaten?" Mr. Breton asked.

"Yup," said the people from the town, "we said that. We think that you are the best cook in the world; we have always thought so."

"Always?" asked Mr. Breton.

"Of course," the people from the town said. "Why do you think we walk seven miles on snowshoes just to eat here?"

The people from the town walked away on their snowshoes. Mr. Breton sat on the edge of the porch and thought it over. When the moose came out to see why Mr. Breton was sitting outside without his coat on, Mr. Breton said, "Do you know, those people think I am the best cook in the whole world?"

"Of course they do," the moose said. "Do you want me to go into town to get some crackers? We seem to have run out."

"Yes," said Mr. Breton, "and get some asparagus too. I'm going to cook something special tomorrow."

"By the way," said the moose, "aren't you cold out here?"

"No, I'm not the least bit cold," Mr. Breton said. "This is turning out to be a very mild winter."

Game Warden

There was a lot of talk in town about the moose at Mr. Breton's restaurant. Some people who had never been there before went to the restaurant just to see the moose. There was an article in the newspaper about the moose, and how he talked to the customers, and brought them their bowls of clam chowder, and helped Mr. Breton in the kitchen.

Some people from other towns drove a long way with chains on their tires to Mr. Breton's restaurant, just to see the moose. Mr. Breton was always very busy waiting on tables at lunchtime and suppertime.

The moose was always very polite to the people, but he made them feel a little uncomfortable too. He looked at people with only one eye at a time, and he was better than most of them at pronouncing French words. Some of the people in the town bragged that the moose was a friend of theirs, and always gave them a table right away. When they came to the restaurant they would pat the moose on the back, and say, "Hello, Moose, you remember me, don't you?"

"There will be a slight delay until a table is ready," the moose would say, and snort, and shake himself.

Mr. Breton was very happy in the kitchen. There were pots of all sorts of good things steaming on the stove and smelling good, and bread baking in the oven from morning to night. Mr. Breton loved to cook good things for lots of people, the more the better. He had never been so busy and happy in his life.

One morning, Mr. Bobowicz, the game warden, came to the restaurant. "Mr. Breton, are you aware of Section 5—Subheading 6—Paragraph 3 of the state fish and game laws?" said Mr. Bobowicz.

"No, I am not aware of Section 5—Subheading 6— Paragraph 3," Mr. Breton said. "What is it all about?"

"No person shall keep a moose as a pet, tie up a moose, keep a moose in a pen or barn, or parlor or bedroom, or any such enclosure," said Mr. Bobowicz. "In short, it is against the law to have a tame moose."

"Oh my," said Mr. Breton, "I don't want to do anything against the law. But I don't keep the moose. He just came along one day, and has stayed ever since. He helps me run my restaurant."

Mr. Bobowicz rubbed his chin. "And where is the aforesaid moose?"

Mr. Breton had given the moose one of the rooms upstairs, in which there was a particularly large bed. The moose just fit in the bed, if he folded up his feet. He liked it very much; he said he never had a bed of his own. The moose slept on the bed under six blankets, and during the day he would go upstairs sometimes, and stretch out on the bed and sigh with pleasure.

When Mr. Bobowicz came to see Mr. Breton, the moose had been downstairs to help Mr. Breton eat a giant breakfast, and then he had wandered back to his room to enjoy lying on his bed until the lunchtime customers arrived. He heard Mr. Breton and Mr. Bobowicz talking. The moose bugled. He had never bugled in Mr. Breton's house before. Bugling is a noise that no animal except a moose can really do right. Elk can bugle, and elephants can bugle, and some kinds of geese and swans can bugle, but it is nothing like moose bugling. When the moose bugled, the whole house jumped and rattled, dishes clinked together in the cupboard, pots and pans clanged together, icicles fell off the house.

"I AM NOT A TAME MOOSE!" the moose shouted from where he was lying on his bed.

Mr. Bobowicz looked at Mr. Breton with very wide eyes. "Was that the moose?"

The moose had gotten out of bed, and was clumping down the stairs. "You're right, that was the moose," he growled.

The moose clumped right up to Mr. Bobowicz, and looked at him with one red eye. The moose's nose was touching Mr. Bobowicz's nose. They just stood there, looking at each other, for a long time. The moose was breathing loudly, and his eye seemed to be a glowing coal. Mr. Bobowicz's knees were shaking. Then the moose spoke very slowly. "You . . . are . . . a . . . tame . . . game warden."

The moose turned, and clumped back up the stairs. Mr. Breton and Mr. Bobowicz heard him sigh and heard the springs crash and groan as he flopped onto the big bed.

"Mr. Bobowicz, the moose is not tame," Mr. Breton said. "He is a wild moose, and he lives here of his own free will; he is the headwaiter." Mr. Breton spoke very quietly, because Mr. Bobowicz had not moved since the moose had come downstairs. His eyes were still open very wide, and his knees were still shaking. Mr. Breton took Mr. Bobowicz by the hand, and led him into the kitchen and poured him a cup of coffee.

Dave

Not very far from Mr. Breton's house, in a secret place in the woods, lived a hermit named Dave. Everybody knew that Dave was out there, but nobody ever saw him. Mr. Bobowicz, the game warden, had seen what might have been Dave a couple of times; or it might have been a shadow. Sometimes, late at night, Mr. Breton would hear the wind whistling strangely, and think of Dave.

The moose brought Dave home with him one night. They were old friends. Dave was dressed in rabbit skins, stitched together. His feet were wrapped in tree bark and moose-moss. An owl sat on his head.

"Dave is very shy," the moose said. "He would appreciate it if you didn't say anything to him until he knows you better, maybe in ten or fifteen years. He knows about your gingerbread, and he would like to try

443

it." While the moose spoke, Dave blushed very red, and tried to cover his face with the owl, which fluttered and squawked.

Mr. Breton put dishes with gingerbread and applesauce and fresh whipped cream in front of Dave, the moose, and the owl. There was no noise but the moose slurping, and Dave's spoon scraping. Mr. Breton turned to get the coffeepot. When he looked back at the table, Dave and the owl were gone.

"Dave says thank you," the moose said.

The next night Dave was back, and this time he had a whistle made out of a turkey bone in his hat. After the gingerbread, Dave played on the whistle, like the wind making strange sounds, the moose hummed, and Mr. Breton clicked two spoons, while the owl hopped up and down on the kitchen table, far into the night.

Hums of a Moose

ne day, after the moose had been staying with Mr. Breton for a fairly long time, there was an especially heavy snowfall. The snow got to be as high as the house, and there was no way for people to come from the town.

Mr. Breton got a big fire going in the stove, and kept adding pieces of wood until the stove was glowing red. The house was warm, and filled with the smell of applesauce, which Mr. Breton was cooking in big pots on the stove. Mr. Breton was peeling apples and the moose was sitting on the floor, lapping every now and then at a big chowder bowl full of coffee on the kitchen table.

The moose didn't say anything. Mr. Breton didn't say anything. Now and then the moose would take a deep breath with his nose in the air, sniffing in the smell of apples and cinnamon and raisins cooking.

Then he would sigh. The sighs got louder and louder.

The moose began to hum—softly, then louder. The humming made the table shake, and Mr. Breton felt the humming in his fingers each time he picked up an apple. The humming mixed with the apple and cinnamon smell and melted the frost on the windows, and the room filled with sunlight. Mr. Breton smelled flowers.

Then he could see them. The kitchen floor had turned into a meadow with new grass, dandelions, periwinkles, and daisies.

The moose hummed. Mr. Breton smelled melting snow. He heard ice cracking. He felt the ground shake under the hoofs of moose returning from the low, wet places. Rabbits bounded through the fields. Bears, thin after the winter's sleep, came out of hiding. Birds sang.

The people in the town could not remember such an unseasonable thaw. The weather got warm all of a sudden, and the ice and snow melted for four days before winter set in again. When they went to Mr. Breton's restaurant, they discovered that he had made a wonderful stew with lots of carrots that reminded them of meadows in springtime.

Moose Moving

When spring finally came, the moose became moody. He spent a lot of time staring out the back door. Flocks of geese flew overhead, returning to lakes in the North, and the moose always stirred when he heard their honking.

"Chef," the moose said one morning, "I will be going tomorrow. I wonder if you would pack some gingerbread for me to take along."

Mr. Breton baked a special batch of gingerbread, and packed it in parcels tied with string, so the moose could hang them from his antlers. When the moose came downstairs, Mr. Breton was sitting in the kitchen drinking coffee. The parcels of gingerbread were on the kitchen table.

"Do you want a bowl of coffee before you go?" Mr.

Breton asked.

"Thank you," said the moose.

"I shall certainly miss you," Mr. Breton said.

"Thank you," said the moose.

"You are the best friend I have," said Mr. Breton.

"Thank you," said the moose.

"Do you suppose you'll ever come back?" Mr. Breton asked.

"Not before Thursday or Friday," said the moose. "It would be impolite to visit my uncle for less than a week."

The moose hooked his antlers into the loops of string on the packages of gingerbread. "My uncle will like this." He stood up and turned to the door.

"Wait!" Mr. Breton shouted. "Do you mean that you are not leaving forever? I thought you were lonely for the life of a wild moose. I thought you wanted to go back to the wild, free places."

"Chef, do you have any idea of how cold it gets in the wild, free places?" the moose said. "And the food! Terrible!"

"Have a nice time at your uncle's," said Mr. Breton.

"I'll send you a postcard," said the moose.

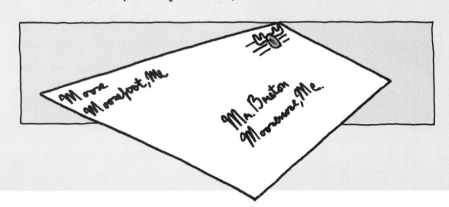

GLOSSARY

Full pronunciation key* The pronunciation of each word is shown just after the word, in this way: **ab·bre·vi·ate** (ə brē′vē āt).

The letters and signs used are pronounced as in the words below.

The mark ′ is placed after a syllable with primary or heavy accent, as in the example above.

The mark ′ after a syllable shows a secondary or lighter accent, as in **ab·bre·vi·a·tion** (ə brē′vē ā′shən).

a	hat, cap	**k**	kind, seek	**ŦH**	then, smooth
ā	age, face	**l**	land, coal		
ä	father, far	**m**	me, am	**u**	cup, butter
		n	no, in	**u̇**	full, put
b	bad, rob	**ng**	long, bring	**ü**	rule, move
ch	child, much				
d	did, red	**o**	hot, rock	**v**	very, save
		ō	open, go	**w**	will, woman
e	let, best	**ô**	order, all	**y**	young, yet
ē	equal, be	**oi**	oil, voice	**z**	zero, breeze
ėr	term, learn	**ou**	house, out	**zh**	measure, seizure
f	fat, if	**p**	paper, cup	**ə**	represents:
g	go, bag	**r**	run, try		a in about
h	he, how	**s**	say, yes		e in taken
		sh	she, rush		i in pencil
i	it, pin	**t**	tell, it		o in lemon
ī	ice, five	**th**	thin, both		u in circus
j	jam, enjoy				

*Pronunciation Key and respellings are from *Scott, Foresman Intermediate Dictionary* by E. L. Thorndike and Clarence L. Barnhart. Copyright © 1979 by Scott, Foresman and Company. Reprinted by permission.

A

a·ban·don (ə ban′dən) *verb.* to give up completely; to withdraw from; desert: *abandon* a sinking ship.

a·brupt (ə brupt′) *adjective.* 1. unexpected change; sudden. 2. steep. 3. blunt; short manner of speech. —**abruptly** *adverb:* The assembly was *abruptly* canceled.

ac·ci·den·tal·ly (ak′sə den′tl ē) *adverb.* happening by chance; not planned.

ac·cur·ate (ak′yər it) *verb.* correct; without mistakes; exact.

ad·ven·ture (ad ven′chər) *noun.* 1. an exciting activity; a thrilling occurrence. 2. an unusual experience.

ad·vice (ad vīs′) *noun.* ideas or suggestions describing what someone should do: My grandmother's *advice* was to apologize to my friend.

ad·vise (ad vīz′) *verb.* 1. to offer advice to; make suggestions: My mother *advised* me to tell Jake I was sorry. 2. to tell; notify. **advised, advising.**

a·gen·cy (ā′jən sē) *noun.* 1. a company or individual acting for another: a travel *agency.* 2. a branch of the government dealing with one kind of work.

a·gree·ment (ə grē′mənt) *noun.* 1. an understanding or contract among people or nations. 2. having similar feelings or opinions.

a·nat·o·my (ə nat′ə mē) *noun.* 1. basic structure of plants or animals. 2. science of the basic structure of plants or animals. **anatomies.**

an·chor (ang′kər) *noun.* heavy piece of metal that keeps a boat stationary in the water. —*verb.* 1. to hold in place by use of an anchor. 2. to stop or maintain position by using an anchor. **anchored, anchoring.**

an·xious (angk′shəs or ang′shəs) *adjective.* 1. worried about something that might happen; nervous. 2. causing uneasy feelings. 3. eager.

ap·par·ent (ə par′ənt) *adjective.* 1. seeming to be real. 2. easy to see or understand: There was no *apparent* reason for being late.

ap·pre·ci·ate (ə prē′shē āt) *verb.* 1. to be thankful for. 2. to understand. 3. to recognize value in. **appreciated, appreciating.**

arch·er·y (är′chər ē) *noun.* sport of shooting with a bow and arrow.

ar·mor (är′mər) *noun.* 1. a protective covering. 2. a suit of material, usually metal, worn to protect someone during fighting. 3. equipment, such as tanks, of the armed forces or military unit.

ar·range (ə ranj′) *verb.* 1. to set up; prepare. 2. to put in correct order. 3. to adapt music in a particular way. **arranged, arranging.**

ar·range·ment (ə rānj′mənt) *noun.* 1. a plan; preparation. 2. an arranging into the correct order. 3. the grouping or order into which something is put: a flower *arrangement.* 4. a settlement. 5. an adaptation of a musical piece.

a·shamed (ə shāmd′) *adjective.* embarrassed; not proud of silly or wrong behavior.

as·ton·ish (ə ston′ish) *verb.* surprise. **astonished, astonishing.**

as·ton·ish·ment (ə ston′ish mənt) *noun.* amazement; surprise.

at·tract (ə trakt′) *verb.* 1. to draw toward; cause to move closer. 2. to win the interest of: *attract* attention.

auc·tion (ôk′shən) *noun.* sale in which items go to the person willing to pay the most money. —*verb.* to sell things at an auction.

au·di·ence (ô′dē əns) *noun.* 1. people who come together to hear or see someone or something. 2. those who listen to television or radio. 3. the right to be listened to. 4. a formal meeting, often with a person of royalty.

au·thor (ô′thər) *noun.* person whose writing is published.

au·to·mat·ic (ô′tə mat′ik) *adjective.* 1. moving without help; acting by itself. 2. natural; done without thought.

B

bam·boo (bam bü′) *noun.* a woody grass, usually with a tall, hollow stem.

bare (ber or bar) *adjective.* 1. naked; not dressed. 2. exposed; not covered. 3. empty. **barer, barest.** —*verb.* to uncover. **bared, baring.**

bar·gain (bär′gən) *noun.* 1. something that is sold or bought at a price that is lower than usual. 2. deal; agreement to trade. —*verb.* to try to buy something cheaply; to try to make a good deal.

base (bās) *noun.* 1. the bottom of anything: the *base* of a statue. 2. center of supply or operation. 3. essential part of something. 4. in some sports, a specific place or goal. —*verb.* to establish; rely upon. —*adjective.* 1. mean; self-ish. 2. of less value than something else.

bis·cuit (bis′kit) *noun.* 1. soft, light bread made with baking powder. 2. a cracker.

bluff (bluf) *noun.* a steep cliff.

blunt (blunt) *adjective.* 1. not sharp; dull. 2. outspoken; not concerned with other peoples' feelings. **blunter, bluntest.** —*verb.* to make dull: He *blunted* the knife when he used it to cut very hard wood. **blunted, blunting.**

boar (bôr) *noun.* 1. a wild pig or hog. 2. male domesticated hog.

boast (bōst) *verb.* 1. to brag; speak too highly of oneself. 2. to have something to be proud of. —*noun.* 1. bragging words. 2. the thing one is proud of.

bog (bog) *noun.* a swamp or marsh area. —*verb.* 1. to sink into a bog. 2. to sink into and get stuck in some difficulty: *bogged* down with chores. **bogged, bogging.**

braid (brād) *verb.* 1. to weave strips of such material as hair or rope: She *braided* her hair. 2. to decorate with braid. **braided, braiding.** —*noun.* a strip formed by weaving hair, rope, or cloth.

brass (bras) *noun.* 1. a metal made of copper and zinc. 2. decorative items made of brass. 3. (plural) musical instruments of metal, such as trumpets and trombones. —*adjective:* a *brass* band.

bul·le·tin (bul′ə tən) *noun.* 1. a brief news item: The weather *bulletin* warned that a storm was on the way. 2. a magazine, usually published by an organization.

bur·y (ber′ē) 1. to put something in the ground and cover it with dirt. 2. to hide or conceal by covering over. 3. to become deeply involved. **buried, burying.**

C

cast (kast) *verb.* 1. to throw; to toss: The fisherman will *cast* his line into the water. 2. to choose for a role in a play. 3. to shape by making a mold. —*noun.* 1. support made of plaster. 2. actors in a play.

cen·tur·y (sen'chər ē) *noun.* 1. a period of 100 years. 2. each period of 100 years. **centuries.**

cham·pi·on·ship (cham'pē ən ship) *noun.* state of being a winner; first place.

chan·nel (chan'l) *noun.* 1. bed of a river: The river cut a *channel* a mile wide into the wilderness. 2. a connecting body of water. —*verb.* to form a channel. **channeled, chaneling** or **channelled, channelling.**

chem·i·cal (kem'ə kəl) *adjective.* having to do with chemistry. —*noun.* substance formed in a chemical process. **chemicals.**

ci·ta·tion (sī tā'shən) *noun.* 1. quotation given. 2. commendation for bravery: The girl's bravery in saving her drowning friend earned her a *citation* from the townspeople. 3. praise for public service. 4. a summons to appear in court.

ci·vil'ian (sə vil'yən) *noun.* a person who is not in any branch of the military service: *Civilians* are not required to salute military officers. **civilians.**

civ·i·li·za·tion (siv'ə lə zā'shən) *noun.* 1. people that have reached a high level of social development. 2. a high degree of social development. 3. the process of reaching a high degree of social development.

clad (klad) *verb.* dressed; clothed: The woman was *clad* in an old-fashioned costume.

clar·i·ty (klar'ə tē) *noun.* clearness: His writing shows *clarity* and imagination.

cli·ent (klī'ənt) *noun.* 1. person receiving a service from a professional: The lawyer discussed the details of the case with his *clients.* 2. a customer.

cli·mate (klī'mit) *noun.* 1. normal weather conditions for a particular area. 2. an area associated with its usual weather conditions. 3. general feeling or atmosphere.

cling (kling) *verb.* 1. to stick or hold to. 2. to adhere to an idea; be faithful to. **clung, clinging.**

clutch (kluch) *verb.* 1. to hold or grip tightly. 2. to snatch; catch hold of. **clutched, clutching.** —*noun.* 1. a grip or hold. 2. a part of a machine that disconnects other moving parts.

cob·ble·stone (kob'əl stōn') *noun.* paving made of naturally-rounded stones: Before tar was used many roads were paved with *cobblestones.*

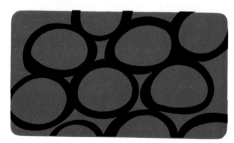

coil (koil) *noun.* 1. loops wound to make such things as wire or rope: a *coil* of rope. 2. one loop in a spiral. 3. a spiral of wire to conduct electricity. —*verb.* to wind into loops.

com·mence (kə mens′) *verb.* to start; begin. **commenced, commencing.**

com·mon (kom′ən) *adjective.* 1. regarding the public or people in general. 2. shared by people. 3. widespread. 4. ordinary: It was *common* for Carlos to stop at the library on his way home from school. 5. coarse; crude. 6. having no special rank. —*noun.* a park near the center of a town.

con·fi·dent (kon′fə dənt) *adjective.* feeling certain; sure.

con·firm (kən fėrm′) *verb.* 1. to show to be true: *confirm* a fact. 2. to strengthen. 3. to approve formally; to ratify. 4. to admit to a religious membership.

con·fu·sion (kən fyü′zhən) *noun.* 1. a state of being confused; uncertainty. 2. disorder: On opening day in the store there was great *confusion* among the clerks. 3. mistaking something for something else.

con·trap·tion (kən trap′shən) *noun.* a gadget or device: The children built the *contraption* from junk they found in the garage.

con·ver·sa·tion (kon′vər sā′shən) *noun.* an oral exchange of thoughts; informal talk.

con·vict (kən vikt′) *verb.* to state that someone is guilty of a crime: The thief was *convicted* of stealing valuable paintings. **convicted, convicting.** —(kon′vikt) *noun.* a person sentenced to prison for committing a crime.

con·vince (kən vins′) *verb.* to make someone do something; assure: You are *convincing* me that you are right and I am wrong. **convinced, convincing.**

coy·o·te (kī ō′tē or kī′ōt) *noun.* small animal, like a wolf, that lives mainly on the western North American prairies. **coyotes.**

crea·ture (krē′chər) *noun.* 1. a person or animal. 2. anything that is made or created. 3. someone under the control of something or someone.

crude (krüd) *adjective.* 1. in a natural state: Before being refined, oil is called *crude* oil. 2. graceless; unpolished; lacking taste. 3. rough, as in art.

D

de·ci·sion (di sizh′ən) *noun.* 1. the act of deciding or making up one's mind; conclusion. 2. report of a conclusion or judgment.

del·i·cate (del′ə kit) *adjective.* 1. pleasing to the senses. 2. easily torn or hurt; fine. 3. needing sensitivity or tact.

de·pot (dē′pō) *noun.* bus or train station. —(dep′ō) military warehouse.

de·pres·sion (di presh′ən) *noun.* 1. a lowering; a movement down. 2. an indentation; a lower place: The heavy barrel left a *depression* in the mud. 3. a state of extreme sadness. 4. a time of reduced economic activity.

de·scend (di send′) *verb.* 1. to go or come down: *descended* from the sky. 2. to go down a (musical) scale. 3. to attack suddenly. 4. to spring from. **descended, descending.**

de·sign·er (di zī′nər) *noun.* someone who plans the structure of a building, project, or pattern: Many famous clothes *designers* come from France. **designers.**

des·per·ate (des′pər it) *adjective.* 1. reckless because of despair: When he realized he was lost a *desperate* feeling overcame him. 2. willing to run any risk. 3. not likely to be cured.

de·tec·tive (di tek′tiv) *noun.* one who works to solve crimes. —*adjective.* 1. relating to detectives and their work. 2. related to discovering something.

de·ter·gent (di tėr′jənt) *noun.* substance used for cleaning: laundry *detergents.* **detergents.**

de·vour (di vour′) *verb.* 1. to eat. 2. to eat quickly, hungrily. 3. to use up; consume: A fire can *devour* a house in a matter of minutes. 4. to absorb.

di·a·gram (dī′ə gram) *noun.* 1. a drawing that shows how the parts of something fit together. 2. a plan or chart. —*verb.* to explain by using a diagram.

di·rec·tor (dī rek′tər or də rek′tər) *noun.* 1. a person who directs or guides an activity: the tour *director.* 2. someone who directs business in a company.

dis·a·gree·ment (dis′ə grē′mənt) *noun.* 1. differing of opinion. 2. argument or quarrel. 3. unlikeness.

dis·card (dis kärd′) *verb.* to throw away as useless: He *discarded* the ripped paper. **discarded, discarding.** —(dis′kärd) *noun.* the thing that is thrown away.

dis·cour·age (dis kėr′ij) *verb.* 1. to take away hope or courage of someone. 2. persuade someone from doing something: Do not try to *discourage* me from climbing the mountain. **discouraged, discouraging.**

dis·guise (dis gīz′) *verb.* 1. to make changes in appearance to look like someone else. 2. to hide what something is; change something to seem like something else: *disguise* your voice. **disguised, dis-**

guising. —*noun.* costume or makeup to change one's appearance.

dis·may (dis mā') *noun.* loss of courage due to fear: He was filled with *dismay* when the project seemed to be failing. —*verb.* to make afraid alarm.

doc·u·ment (dok'yə mənt) *noun.* a written paper showing true information: Birth certificates are important *documents.* —(dok'yə ment) *verb.* to support with proof.

dread (dred) *verb.* to worry or fear that something will happen: I *dreaded* going out in the cold. **dreaded, dreading.** —*noun.* the worry about an event feared likely to happen.

dread·ful (dred'fəl) *adjective.* terrible; unpleasant.

dredge (drej) *verb.* to gather things from the bottom of a river or lake; to clean: They are *dredging* the river for the capsized rowboat. **dredged, dredging.** —*noun.* equipment used in dredging.

drift (drift) *verb.* 1. to float away by wind or water. 2. to wander. 3. to pile up from the effect of wind or water. —*noun.* 1. a pile left by wind or water: I could hardly see over the snow *drifts* that were left by the storm. 2. the act of being carried by wind or water. 3. meaning of what someone says or implies. **drifts.**

dwell (dwel) *verb.* 1. to live: They *dwell* in the country. 2. (with, on) to think or talk about for a long time.

E

ef·fi·cient (ə fish'ənt) *adjective.* capable; carrying out a project with little wasted time or energy: an *efficient* worker.

el·der·ly (el'dər lē) *adjective.* somewhat old.

e·lect (i lekt') *verb.* 1. to vote into office. 2. to select; to choose. **elected, electing.**

e·nor·mous (i nôr'məs) *adjective.* huge.

en·thu·si·asm (en thü'zē az'əm) *noun.* eagerness; excitement: Her *enthusiasm* over the good news spread through the crowd.

en·tire (en tīr') *adjective.* complete; whole; containing all parts: an *entire* day.

es·ca·la·tor (es'kə lā'tər) *noun.* stairs that move so that people can glide up or down without actually walking.

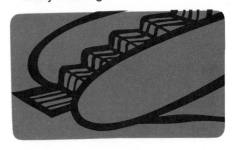

ex·cite·ment (ek sīt'mənt) *noun.* 1. a state of being aroused or excited. 2. anything that excites.

ex·claim (ek sklām') *verb.* to cry out; to shout. **exclaimed, exclaiming.**

ex·haust (eg zôst') *noun.* 1. gas given off by an engine: car *exhaust.* 2. a pipe through which gas escapes. —*verb.* 1. to make tired. 2. to use up; to consume.

ex·haust·ed (eg zô'stid) *adjective.* very tired.

ex·per·i·ment (ek sper'ə mənt) *noun.* a test to prove something or gain new knowledge: scientific *experiments.* —(ek sper'ə ment) *verb.* to make tests or trials.

ex·pla·na·tion (ek'splə nā'shən) *noun.* 1. the act of telling the meaning: She gave a good *explanation* of how to fix a flat bicycle tire. 2. something that tells the meaning of.

ex·plode (ek splōd') *verb.* 1. to burst noisily or suddenly. 2. to cause to burst. **exploded, exploding.**

ex·traor·di·nar·y (ek strôr'də ner'ē) *adjective.* unusual; more than ordinary: She has an *extraordinary* sense of humor.

F

fab·ric (fab'rik) *noun.* material or cloth.

fail·ure (fā'lyər) *noun.* 1. the act of failing. 2. the act of neglect. 3. not having enough. 4. loss of strength. 5. going bankrupt. 6. a person or thing that fails.

fal·ter (fôl'tər) *verb.* 1. to stumble; to make an unsteady movement: The ballet dancer *faltered* while trying to complete a difficult step. 2. to stammer; to talk in a broken manner. 3. to hesitate. **faltered, faltering.**

fa·mil·iar (fə mil'yər) *adjective.* 1. common; recognizable; well-known. 2. understand; knowledgable about: The tourists were not *familiar* with the French language. 3. informed.

fan·cy (fan'sē) *noun.* 1. imagination. 2. preference. **fancies.** —*adjective.* 1. of high quality. 2. not plain; elaborate. **fancier, fanciest.** —*verb.* 1. to imagine: Do you *fancy* yourself a champion swimmer? 2. to suppose. 3. to like; be fond of. **fancied, fancying.**

fare (fer or far) *noun.* 1. the price charged for transportation on such vehicles as buses and planes. 2. a paying passenger. —*verb.* to succeed; to get along: She will *fare* well on her trip. **fared, faring.**

fee·ble (fē'bəl) *adjective.* weak; having little strength. **feebler, feeblest.**

fer·tile (fėr'tl) *adjective.* 1. able to produce or bear something. 2.

rich; fruitful: *fertile* soil. 3. creative; producing ideas.

fer·ti·liz·er (fėr′tl ī′zər) *noun.* something that helps plants grow: Each spring the farmer spreads different *fertilizers* on his fields. **fertilizers.**

fierce (firs) *adjective.* 1. ferocious; wild; daring: the *fierce* tiger. 2. raging. 3. active. **fiercer, fiercest.**

flour·ish (flėr′ish) *verb.* 1. to thrive; grow well. 2. to wave, as a flag; to make sweeping movements. —*noun.* 1. a sweeping movement. 2. a flashy display. 3. a fancy or added decoration: He signed his name with a *flourish.* 4. a showy passage of music.

fo·reign (fôr′ən) *adjective.* 1. regarding a country different from one's own: a *foreign* country. 2. relating to or dealing with other countries. 3. not fitting in, not related.

for·mer (fôr′mər) *adjective.* 1. first of two. 2. occurring in any earlier time past: the *former* president.

forth (fôrth) *adverb.* 1. forward: back and *forth.* 2. into sight.

fringe (frinj) *noun.* 1. a border or trim of bunched threads. 2. a border. —*verb.* to be a border to. —**fringed** *adjective:* Put the *fringed* tablecloth on the table.

func·tion (fungk′shən) *noun.* 1. purpose; proper action of something: The *function* of a key is to unlock

doors. 2. a formal party, ceremony, or social gathering. —*verb.* to act as.

fur·i·ous (fyůr′ē əs) *adjective.* very angry; intense. —**furiously** *adverb.*

G

gauze (gôz) *noun.* thin, loosely woven cloth: The doctor used *gauze* to bandage my cut knee.

ge·og·ra·phy (jē og′rə fē) *noun.* 1. the study of the earth's surface, climate, resources, people. 2. a book relating to this study. 3. natural features.

gin·ger (jin′jər) *noun.* a spice made from the root of a tropical plant.

glim·mer (glim′ər) *noun.* 1. a faint beam of light: a *glimmer* of light. 2. slight feeling. —*verb.* to shine faintly.

glimpse (glimps) *noun.* a quick look. —*verb.* to take a quick look: *glimpse* the headlines. **glimpsed, glimpsing.**

glis·ten (glis′n) *verb.* to shine or sparkle: The stars *glistened* in the sky. **glistened, glistening.** —*noun.* a sparkle.

463

gov·ern·ment (guv′ərn mənt) *noun.*
1. rule of a country, state, city, or town. 2. those who rule such entities. 3. form or system of ruling.
—*adjective.* relating or belonging to the rule of a country: a *government* building.

graze (grāz) *verb.* to eat grass. **grazed, grazing.**

grieve (grēv) *verb.* 1. to feel sad: I *grieved* when my pet died. 2. to cause to suffer; to make sad. **grieved, grieving.**

grove (grōv) *noun.* a group of trees: an orange *grove.* **groves.**

guard·i·an (gär′dē ən) *noun.* 1. someone who takes care of or protects something: She is the *guardian* of the valuable pieces of art at the museum. 2. a person appointed by the law to take care of either someone young (a minor) or someone who cannot care for himself or herself.

H

halt (hôlt) *verb.* to bring to a stop. —*noun.* a stop.

has·ten (hā′sn) *verb.* to hurry; go quickly: Water and fertilizer will *hasten* a plant's growth. **hastened, hastening.**

haul (hôl) *verb.* 1. to pull or drag. 2. to carry; transport. **hauled, hauling.** —*noun.* 1. the things being carried or taken. 2. act of pulling or dragging. 3. distance goods are carried.

heart·y (här′tē) *adjective.* 1. having much to eat: a *hearty* appetite. 2. cheerful; full of energy. 3. in good health. **heartier, heartiest.** —**heartily** *adverb.*

heed (hēd) *noun.* consideration; attention: Drivers should pay *heed* to posted speed limits. —*verb.* to give consideration to; give notice to.

herb (ėrb or hėrb) *noun.* 1. plant whose parts are used in spices, medicine, foods. 2. a flowering plant whose stem lives just one season.

her·it·age (her′ə tij) *noun.* 1. an inheritance; something willed to a person from another, usually a relative. 2. traditions or customs passed down from generation to generation: Thanksgiving dinner is part of the American *heritage.*

hes·i·tant (hez′ə tənt) *adjective.* undecided; doubtful; hesitating. —**hesitantly** *adverb:* She knocked *hesitantly* on her neighbor's door.

hes·i·tate (hez'ə tāt) *verb.* 1. to be uncertain or undecided. 2. to be unwilling. 3. to pause or stop. 4. to speak with pauses. **hesitated, hesitating.**

hind (hīnd) *adjective.* in back; rear: *hind* legs.

hol·low (hol'ō) *adjective.* 1. not solid, having a hole inside. 2. curved inward; shaped like a bowl. 3. having a deep sound. 4. false; worthless. —*noun.* 1. hole; empty place. 2. valley; low place between hills. —*verb.* to dig out or make a hole inside of.

hon·or (on'ər) *noun.* 1. credit for acting well; fame; glory: He got the award in *honor* of his excellent work. 2. source of credit; something that is cause of praise. 3. good reputation; sense of what is right. 4. respect. 5. (Honor) title of respect. 6. (honors) recognition to a student whose work is very well done. 7. (honors) an act of respect. —*verb.* 1. to respect; think highly of. 2. to accept in payment.

I

i·den·ti·fy (ī den'tə fī) *verb.* 1. to determine who or what a person or thing is. 2. connect closely; associate. **identified, identifying.**

il·lus·trate (il'ə strāt or i lus'trāt) *verb.* 1. to explain using stories or examples. 2. to provide with such things as pictures, drawings, or maps to explain or decorate: *illustrate* a book. **illustrated, illustrating.**

im·me·di·ate·ly (i mē'dē it lē) *adverb.* 1. right away; with haste. 2. right after; with nothing intervening.

im·pa·tient (im pā'shənt) *adjective.* 1. not patient; not willing to cope with delay. 2. restless; uneasy. —**impatiently** *adverb:* The children waited *impatiently* for the movie to begin.

im·press (im pres') *verb.* 1. to influence: I was *impressed* by her skill in horseback riding. 2. to put firmly in one's mind. 3. to stamp; press marks on. **impressed, impressing.** —(im'pres) *noun.* mark made by pressing or stamping.

in·dig·ni·ty (in dig'nə tē) *noun.* an insult; poor treatment: It is easier to suffer an *indignity* in a play than in real life.

i·ni·tial (i nish'əl) *adjective.* 1. first; coming at the beginning. —*noun.* 2. the first letter of a word or of a proper name: middle *initial.* —*verb.* to write the initials of.

in·no·cent (in'ə sənt) *adjective.* 1. free from guilt or wrongdoing: At the end of the trial, the jury found the person *innocent.* 2. natural, sincere. 3. causing no harm.

in·ten·tion (in ten'shən) *noun.* pur-

465

pose; idea; good plan: Their *intention* is to go to Los Angeles for their vacation.

in·ter·rupt (in'tə rupt') *verb.* 1. to cause a break; put a stop to temporarily. 2. to halt the actions of another. **interrupted, interrupting.**

in·ves·ti·gate (in ves'tə gāt) *verb.* to study by close examination; look into carefully: Divers *investigated* the ocean floor. **investigated, investigating.**

in·volve (in volv') *verb.* 1. to become occupied or interested: After taking part in the school play, she became *involved* in acting. 2. to include. 3. to draw into a situation. **involved, involving.**

J

jour·nal (jėr'nl) *noun.* 1. a daily account of activities and events: a daily *journal.* 2. a magazine or newspaper.

jour·ney (jėr'nē) *noun.* 1. travel or trip. 2. distance that has been traveled. **journeys.** —*verb.* to travel.

K

keen (kēn) *adjective.* 1. sharp. 2. cutting; sharp-like. 3. sensitive; highly developed: She has *keen* sight and hearing. 4. interested in; enthusiastic about.

L

lan·tern (lan'tərn) *noun.* an instrument made of glass and metal giving off light by use of a flame or bulb.

lap (lap) *noun.* 1. the flat surface of the upper part of the legs on a person sitting down. 2. once around a racetrack. —*verb.* 1. to drink by extending the tongue. 2. to hit or splash softly: The waves were *lapping* gently against the shore. **lapped, lapping.** —**lapping** *adjective.*

lav·en·der (lav'ən dər) *adjective.* purple color. —*noun.* a shrub with purple flowers used in making perfume.

league (lēg) *noun.* 1. a group formed for a common purpose: a baseball *league.* 2. group of members of a sport. 3. unit of measurement.

ledge (lej) *noun.* a narrow shelf or ridge: a rocky *ledge.*

li·cense (lī′sns) *noun.* 1. permission granted to do something. 2. card or plate showing permission: a marriage *license.*

limb (lim) *noun.* 1. a big branch: tree *limbs.* 2. leg, arm, wing. **limbs.**

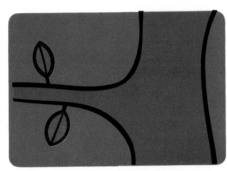

liq·uid (lik′wid) *noun.* a fluid; a substance that flows, such as water. —*adjective.* 1. melted, like a liquid. 2. flowing smoothly or easily. 3. easily transferred into cash.

loaf (lōf) *noun.* a mass of food molded into an oblong shape, such as a *loaf* of bread. —*verb.* to waste time: Saturday afternoons can be a good time for *loafing.* **loafed, loafing.**

lodge (loj) *verb.* 1. to stay overnight or provide a place to stay. 2. to make or file, as a complaint. 3. to become stuck: My ankle became *lodged* between two branches of the tree. **lodged, lodging.** —*noun.* 1. a place to stay. 2. a cabin often used by hunters. 3. a branch of a secret society.

loom (lüm) *noun.* a frame or machine for weaving cloth. —*verb.* to appear in a strange or threatening way.

M

ma·gi·cian (mə jish′ən) *noun.* 1. a person who does things by magic. 2. someone who performs magic tricks to entertain others.

mag·nif·i·cent (mag nif′ə sənt) *adjective.* impressive; grand; majestic: a *magnificent* sight.

maid·en (mād′n) *noun.* girl; unmarried woman. —*adjective.* 1. first. 2. unmarried.

mal′lard (mal′ərd) *noun.* a wild duck. —**mallards** or **mallard** *plural.*

mar·vel (mär′vəl) *noun.* something that causes wonder. —*verb.* to feel astonishment; to be filled with surprise: He *marveled* at the beautiful music that was played on the harp. **marveled, marveling** or **marvelled, marvelling.**

mar·vel·ous (mär′və ləs) *adjective.* 1. wonderful. 2. unlikely; improbable.

mech·a·nism (mek′ə niz′əm) *noun.* 1. machine or parts of a machine: The *mechanism* for winding the clock was broken. 2. parts working together as parts on a machine.

min·now (min′ō) *noun.* a very small

467

fish. **—minnows** or **minnow** *plural.*

mo·squi·to (mə skē′tō) *noun.* a long-legged, flying insect. **—mosquitoes** or **mosquitos** *plural.*

mo·tion (mō′shən) *noun.* 1. act of moving; change of position. 2. a suggestion, made during a meeting, that must be voted on. *—verb.* to make a movement.

muf·fle (muf′əl) *verb.* 1. to wrap in something to deaden the sound. 2. to make a sound softer: She *muffled* her laughter as her friends approached her secret hideaway. **muffled, muffling.**

muf·fler (muf′lər) *noun.* 1. a scarf worn around the neck for warmth: a wool *muffler.* 2. anything used to deaden sound, such as a car *muffler.*

mu·si·cian (myü zish′ən) *noun.* a person who plays a musical instrument well; a composer; a singer.

N

nar·ra·tor (nar′ā tər or na rā′tər) *noun.* someone who tells a story: The *narrator* of the radio program told what the radio play was about.

na·tion·al (nash′ə nəl) *adjective.* related to a nation: the *national* anthem. *—noun.* a citizen of a nation.

ner·vous (nėr′vəs) *adjective.* 1. related to nerves, such as a *nervous* feeling. 2. restless. 3. fearful.

no·tion (nō′shən) *noun.* 1. an idea. 2. a theory. 3. a desire or whim. 4. (plural) small articles such as ribbons, thread, pins: Fabric stores sell buttons and other *notions.* **notions.**

numb (num) *adjective.* having no feeling: *numb* with cold.

O

ob·jec·tion (əb jek′shən) *noun.* 1. a reason to dislike someone or something. 2. a feeling against something: Her mother had no *objection* to her going to the party.

o·rig·i·nal (ə rij′ə nəl) *adjective.* 1. new; fresh: an *original* idea. 2. creative; inventive. 3. first. *—noun.* the first form of something from which others may be copied.

ox·en (ok′sən) *noun.* plural of ox; full grown male members of cattle family used for farm work, such as plowing.

palm (päm) *noun.* 1. a tall tree or shrub with leaves at the top that grows in warm climates. 2. a leaf from a palm tree usually used as a symbol of victory.

par·cel (pär′səl) *noun.* 1. a package. 2. piece, as of land. 3. a group of; pack. **parcels.**

par·ti·cle (pär′tə kəl) *noun.* a very small piece of something: dust *particles.* **particles.**

par·tic·u·lar·ly (pər tik′yə lər lē) *adverb.* 1. especially: They enjoy camping, *particularly* in parks that have lakes. 2. with emphasis. 3. in a certain way.

part·ner·ship (pärt′nər ship) *noun.* the state of being a partner; a business relationship of joint interest: The two women decided to work together in a *partnership.*

pat·ent (pat′nt) *noun.* a document giving an inventor sales rights to an invention for a certain time period. —*verb.* to get a patent for. —*adjective.* 1. something patented. Those *patent* movable bookcases are expensive. 2. plain; evident.

pause (pôz) *noun.* 1. a brief stop or wait. 2. a sign used in music to show that a note or rest is to be held.

pe·cul·iar (pi kyü′lyər) *adjective.* 1. strange or odd: A dictionary without words would be *peculiar.* 2. relating solely to; special.

ped·dler (ped′lər) *noun.* a person who moves from place to place selling goods: The *peddlers* sell their goods on the corner. **peddlers.**

peer (pir) *verb.* 1. to look at closely in order to see: *peer* out a window. 2. to come out.

per·son·al·i·ty (pėr′sə nal′ə tē) *noun.* 1. the special characteristics or qualities that make people the way they are: Although the twins look exactly alike, they have different *personalities.* 2. a well-known person. **personalities.**

pho·to·graph (fō'tə graf) *noun.* an image or picture made using a camera. **photographs.** —*verb.* to take a photograph of.

phrase (frāz) *noun.* 1. expression people use: "Cool as a cucumber" is a *phrase* some people use. 2. group of words without a subject and predicate. 3. a few measures or sections of music. —*verb.* to express in a certain way.

piece (pēs) *noun.* 1. one of the parts of a whole. 2. a single thing of a set or collection. 3. limited part; portion. 4. quantity; section. 5. a creative work: *pieces* of artwork. 6. an example of something. 7. a coin. **pieces.** —*verb.* 1. to make by joining pieces. 2. to join pieces of something.

pi·geon·hole (pij'ən hōl') *noun.* 1. a place where pigeons nest. 2. a slot in a desk organizer for office supplies: The clerk arranged envelopes and note paper in the *pigeonholes* in his desk. —*verb.* 1. to put into a pigeonhole. 2. to put off so as to forget.

pi·o·neer (pī' ə nir') *noun.* 1. person who does something first. 2 person who moves to an unsettled part of a country: The *pioneers* moved west in covered wagons. **pioneers.** —*verb.* to do something first.

plain (plān) *noun.* flat land: The wild horses roamed the *plain* looking for food. —*adjective.* 1. easily understood. 2. bare; unadorned. 3. ordinary.

play·wright (plā'rīt') *noun.* someone who writes plays: William Shakespeare was a famous *playwright.*

plight (plīt) *noun.* a difficult or bad situation: People contributed money to help her out of her *plight.* —*verb.* to promise; pledge.

plunge (plunj) *verb.* 1. to thrust or throw into. 2. move; rush: The swimmer *plunged* into the pool. **plunged, plunging.** —*noun.* a jump or dive.

pol·len (pol'ən) *noun.* yellowish powder found on flowers: In springtime there is a lot of *pollen* in the air.

pos·se (pos'ē) *noun.* a group of people organized by a sheriff to maintain law and order: The *posse* followed the trail of the fleeing bank robber.

prair·ie (prer'ē) *noun.* large grassland area with few trees.

pre·cious (presh'əs) *adjective.* 1. very valuable; of great worth: *precious* jewels. 2. held dear; loved.

prop·er·ly (prop'ər lē) *adverb.* 1. in a proper or correct manner: You are not dressed *properly* for such cold weather. 2. rightly; justly. 3. strictly.

pub·lish·er (pub′li shər) *noun.* person or company who prints or sells books, newspapers, magazines, or other such material.

pur·chase (pėr′chəs) *verb.* to buy. —*noun.* 1. an item that is bought. 2. the act of buying. 3. a tight grip.

pyr·a·mid (pir′ə mid) *noun.* 1. a four-sided figure having triangular sides that meet at the top. 2. a monument with that shape: The ancient Egyptians built huge *pyramids* out of stone. —*verb.* to make into the form of a pyramid.

Q

quiv·er (kwiv′ər) *verb.* to shake or tremble. —*noun.* 1. a shaking: A *quiver* in the man's hand caused him to drop the dish. 2. a case for keeping arrows.

R

ra·di·ant (rā′dē ənt) *adjective.* 1. shining; glowing: His face was *radiant* when he heard the good news. 2. coming from rays.

rec·og·nize (rek′əg nīz) *verb.* 1. to acknowledge acquaintance with. 2. to acknowledge formally. 3. to know upon sight or hearing. **recognized, recognizing.**

reed (rēd) *noun.* 1. a tall grass usually found in wetlands: The water snake slithered through the *reeds* of the marsh. 2. a musical pipe. 3. a piece of wood used in the mouthpiece of a musical instrument, such as a clarinet. **reeds.**

re·flect (ri flekt′) *verb.* 1. to give back an image of: *reflected* in a mirror. 2. to show; reproduce. 3. to throw back, such as heat. 4. to think carefully. **reflected, reflecting.**

rel·a·tive (rel′ə tiv) *noun.* a person who is part of your larger family, such as a cousin; kin. **relatives.** —*adjective.* 1. connected or related. 2. comparable to something else.

re·lieve (ri lēv′) *verb.* 1. to lessen or ease pain or worry: I am *relieved* to find out that Mary found her lost puppy. 2. to give aid. 3. to take over a shift or duty. 4. to give contrast or variety.

re·ly (ri lī′) *verb.* to depend on or trust in: You can *rely* on her to do a thorough job. **relied, relying.**

rem·e·dy (rem′ə dē) *noun.* a cure: a cold *remedy.* **remedies.** —*verb.* to cure.

471

re·quest (re kwest′) *noun.* 1. the act of asking for something: At the library she made a *request* for a special book. 2. the thing asked for. —*verb.* to ask for something.

re·sort (ri zôrt′) *verb.* to go for help. —*noun.* 1. somewhere people go, usually for vacation: a mountain *resort.* 2. person to whom one goes for help.

re·spond (ri spond′) *verb.* 1. to give an answer; to reply: *responded* to a question. 2. to react to. **responded, responding.**

res·taur·ant (res′tər ent or res′tə ränt) *noun.* a place where a person can buy a meal and eat it.

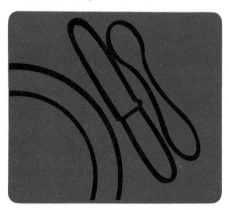

re·verse (ri vèrs′) *adjective.* 1. opposite or backward. 2. causing backward movement. —*noun.* 1. the opposite of. 2. a change for the worse. —*verb.* 1. to move backward. 2. to turn to the opposite position. 3. to change a decision. **reversed, reversing.**

rum·ble (rum′bəl) *noun.* a low heavy continuous sound: the *rumble* of thunder. —*verb.* to move with a low heavy continuous sound. **rumbled, rumbling.**

rum·ple (rum′pəl) *verb.* to wrinkle; crumple: I *rumpled* up the paper and threw it away. **rumpled, rumpling.**

run·way (run′wā) *noun.* 1. the part of an airport on which planes take off and land. 2. a path made by or for animals.

S

scar·let (skär′lit) *noun* or *adjective.* very bright red.

scour (skour) *verb.* 1. to clean or polish by rubbing. 2. to clean thoroughly. 3. to search thoroughly. 4. to move quickly over: The heavy rain *scoured* the flatlands. **scoured, scouring.**

seize (sēz) *verb.* 1. to take hold of suddenly. 2. to capture. 3. to take possession with one's mind. **seized, seizing.**

sel·dom (sel′dəm) *adverb.* not often; rarely: She *seldom* forgets to do her homework.

sheathe (shēth) *verb.* 1. to put something (such as a sword) into a case or covering: The soldier *sheathed* his sword as a sign of friendship. 2. enclose in a case or covering. **sheathed, sheathing.**

shel·ter (shel'tər) *noun.* something that covers or gives protection. —*verb.* to protect.

shriek (shrēk) *noun.* a loud, shrill sound. —*verb.* to make a loud, shrill sound. **—shrieking** *adjective.*

shrill (shril) *adjective.* high or piercing: That bird has a *shrill* call. —*noun.* a high sound.

shut·ter (shut'ər) *noun.* 1. protective covering for a window. 2. a cover for closing an opening, such as a shutter in a camera lens.

sig'nal (sig'nəl) *noun.* 1. a sign that warns or informs. 2. messages or images transmitted by radio, television, or telegraph. —*verb.* to make a sign or signal. **signaled, signaling** or **signalled, signalling.**

sim·i·lar·i·ty (sim'ə lar'ə tē) *noun.* likeness; resemblance: The *similarity* of your voice to your brother's voice is unbelievable. **similarities.**

sketch (skech) *noun.* 1. an outline; rough drawing. 2. a short written work, such as a play. **sketches.** —*verb.* to draw roughly. **sketched, sketching.**

skip·per (skip'ər) *noun.* 1. captain of a boat or vessel. 2. any leader.

smoth·er (smuŦH'ər) *verb.* 1. to keep from receiving enough air to breathe: The man felt as if he were *smothering* in the hot, stuffy room. 2. cover with a considerable amount. **smother, smothering.**

so·lu·tion (sə lü'shən) *noun.* 1. the answer to a problem or mystery: the *solution* to the mystery. 2. the process of finding an answer. 3. a mixture combining a solid or a gas with a liquid. 4. the process of forming a mixture.

soothe (süŦH) *verb.* 1. to comfort. 2. to relieve pain: He will try to *soothe* the crying boy with his gentle words. **soothed, soothing.**

sooth·ing (sü'ŦHing) *adjective.* comforting; making less painful.

473

sor·row (sor′ō) *noun.* 1. sadness or grief. 2. cause of grief; regret. —*verb.* to feel or show grief.

spe·cial·ty (spesh′əl tē) *noun.* 1. something done well. 2. a limited type of work: Her *specialty* was arranging flowers in bouquets.

spec·ta·tor (spek′tā tər) *noun.* a person who watches an activity, but does not take part. **spectators.**

spin·dle (spin′dl) *noun.* 1. the pin used in spinning for winding the thread: She is winding the thread onto the *spindle.* 2. any rod or pin that turns. 3. anything shaped like a spindle. —*verb.* to grow tall and slender.

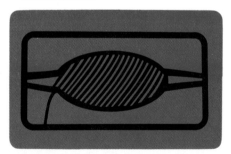

splen·did (splen′did) *adjective.* 1. beautiful; magnificent: The *splendid* throne was made of beautifully carved wood. 2. very good.

staff (staf) *noun.* 1. a group of people working under a director in a company or institution: the *staff* of doctors. 2. a stick used for support. —*verb.* to provide with workers.

stall (stôl) *noun.* 1. section in a stable for an animal: a horse *stall.* 2. a booth where things are sold. 3. a bench. 4. a delay. —*verb.* 1. to stop. 2. to slow down.

steer (stir) *verb.* 1. to guide; control: *Steer* the ship away from the path of oncoming boats. 2. set a course for.

stern (stėrn) *adjective.* 1. harsh; strict; unpleasant: I could tell from the *stern* look on his face that he was angry. 2. severe. —*noun.* the rear of a boat or airplane. — **sternly** *adverb:* The man *sternly* warned us not to touch the electrical wires.

strand (strand) *verb.* 1. to remain helpless away from home. 2. to run on ground or shore: The small craft was *stranded* on the sandbar. **stranded, stranding.** —*noun.* land bordering a body of water.

stride (strīd) *verb.* 1. to take long steps. 2. to take one long step over. **strode, stridden, striding.** —*noun.* a long step: The runner raced ahead as she took longer and longer *strides.* **strides.**

struc·ture (struk′chər) *noun.* 1. building; constructed form: The skyscraper was the tallest *structure* in the city. 2. something made up of parts. 3. the way in which a building is constructed.

strut (strut) *verb.* to walk about

proudly: The rooster *strutted* around the yard. **strutted, strutting.**

stu·di·o (stü′dē ō or styü′dē ō) *noun.* 1. a workroom of an artist. 2. a place where motion pictures or radio and television programs are developed.

stuff·y (stuf′ē) *adjective.* 1. lacking fresh air: When we came home from our vacation, our house was very *stuffy*. 2. blocked up (*stuffy* nose). 3. dull (*stuffy* person).

sub·ject (sub′jikt) *noun.* 1. something being discussed or thought about. 2. person under the power of a government or ruler: the king's *subjects*. 3. course of study. —*adjective.* 1. under power to one or something. 2. likely to have or to get, as a cold. —(səb jekt′) *verb.* to cause to experience something.

suc·cess (sək ses′) *noun.* 1. achievement of what one has worked and hoped for. 2. a person or a thing that does succeed.

sus·pect (sə spekt′) *verb.* 1. to think someone is guilty without proof. 2. to have doubts. 3. to think something is true or likely: When my puppy did not eat, I *suspected* he was sick. **suspected, suspecting.** —(sus′pekt) *noun.* someone who is thought guilty; one suspected.

sus·pi·cious (sə spish′əs) *adjective.* 1. causing one to doubt or suspect: My friend's *suspicious* looks gave away the secret. 2. showing or feeling suspicion. —**suspiciously** *adverb.*

swift (swift) *adjective.* 1. moving quickly. 2. occurring quickly. —*noun.* a bird with long wings.

T

taut (tôt) *adjective.* 1. pulled tightly: a *taut* rope. 2. neat; uncluttered.

tem·per·a·ture (tem′pər ə chər) *noun.* 1. measurement of heat or coldness. 2. measurement of body heat; fever.

tem·ple (tem′pəl) *noun.* 1. building used for worship. 2. a synagogue.

till·er (til′ər) *noun.* 1. part of a boat used in turning the rudder for steering: She turned the *tiller* sharply to the left to avoid hitting the rocks. 2. one who tills or prepares the land for crops.

tim·id (tim′id) *adjective.* lacking courage; shy; fearful: The *timid* child slowly poked his head around the door.

toll (tōl) *verb.* to make a slow, single sound with regular repetition: The bell *tolled* six times. **tolled, tolling.** —*noun* 1. a fee paid to gain access to something. 2. a fee for an extra service, as a toll charged for making a long distance telephone call.

tow·er·ing (tou′ər ing) *adjective.* 1. high; tall: a *towering* building. 2. great; considerable, as a *towering* accomplishment. 3. violent; wild.

trans·late (tran slāt′ or tran′slāt) *verb.* 1. change from one language to another: The Hans Christian Andersen stories have been *translated* from Danish into many other languages. 2. to change form of; express in another form. 3. to explain. **translated, translating.**

tri·um·phant (trī um′fənt) *adjective.* 1. successful; victorious. 2. rejoicing over victory. —**triumphantly** *adverb:* The winners of the spelling contest *triumphantly* received their awards.

trudge (truj) *noun.* a long, weary walk. —*verb.* to walk steadily with effort: She *trudged* through the pouring rain and wind. **trudged, trudging.**

V

vain (vān) *adjective.* 1. having no real value. 2. conceited; having too much pride in oneself. —**in vain.** without success: He tried in *vain* to lift the heavy log.

val·u·a·ble (val′yü ə bəl or val′yə bəl) *adjective.* 1. having value or worth: The Constitution is a *valuable* document. 2. worth a considerable amount of money. —*noun.* (plural) items of value or worth.

vanish (van′ish) *verb.* 1. disappear suddenly: The cat *vanished* from sight. 2. to pass out of existence. **vanished, vanishing.**

var·y (ver′ē or var′ē) *verb.* 1. to make or become different. 2. to be different: Although the children *vary* in age, they get along well with each other. 3. to set up changes in. **varied, varying.**

ven·ture (ven′chər) *noun.* an undertaking that is unsure or risky. —*verb.* 1. to risk; take a chance. 2. to dare, in the sense of an opinion. 3. to dare to come or go: On her first day in the new neighborhood, Sandy wanted to *venture* out and make new friends. **ventured, venturing.**

ve·ran·da (və ran′də) *noun.* a large porch with a roof.

vi·ta·min (vī′ tə mən) *noun.* a substance found in foods that is necessary for growth and good health.

vow (vou) *verb.* to promise; swear under oath: The doctor *vowed* always to treat her patients to the best of her ability. **vowed, vowing.** —*noun.* 1. a pledge or a promise. 2. an official pledge.

voy·age (voi′ij) *noun.* a trip or journey, particularly by sea: a *voyage* around the world.

W

wear·y (wir′ē) *adjective.* tired. **wearier, weariest.** —*verb.* to make tired.

weave (wēv) *verb.* 1. to make an item such as a basket by overlapping strands. 2. to put together, as to *weave* a story. 3. to wind in and out of: The children almost lost their way as they *weaved* in and out of the crowd. **weaved or**

wove, weaving.

wedge (wej) *noun.* 1. piece of wood or metal narrowing to a sharp edge, used to split logs, raise loads, and do other jobs. 2. anything shaped like or used as a wedge. —*verb.* 1. squeeze; force into a small space: He *wedged* the piece of wood into the opening. 2. to make something fit; tighten into place. 3. to split or separate using a wedge. **wedged, wedging.**

whirl (hwėrl) *verb.* 1. to move in circles; to travel. 2. to move very fast. 3. to spin. —*noun.* 1. a rapid circular motion. 2. a series of events. 3. a feeling of confusion. —**whirling** *adjective:* a *whirling* top.

wrap (rap) *verb.* 1. to cover with paper. 2. to wind around. **wrapped** or **wrapt, wrapping.** —*noun.* a coat or outer wear: We got our *wraps* from the closet and prepared to go outside. **wraps.**

477

(Acknowledgments continued from page 2)

Tall Tales by Sid Fleischman. Text copyright © 1978 by Sid Fleischman. Reprinted by permission of Bill Berger Associates, Inc.

Karleen Bradford for the adaptation of her story "The Visitor." Appeared originally in the Spring 1977 issue of Canadian Children's Magazine. Used by permission of the author.

Curtis Brown, Ltd., New York, for "So You Want to Write Bad Jokes!" from Jokes to Read in the Dark by Scott Corbett. Reprinted by permission of Curtis Brown, Ltd. Text copyright © 1980 by Scott Corbett. Also for "Last Days of Brightness," Parts 1 and 2, by David Budbill. Adapted from Snowshoe Trek to Otter River by David Budbill. Text copyright © 1976 by David Budbill. Reprinted with permission of Curtis Brown, Ltd.

Childrens Press, Chicago, for "The Mystery of the Rolltop Desk," adapted from The Mystery of the Rolltop Desk by Evelyn Witter. Copyright © 1977 by Regensteiner Publishing Enterprises, Inc. Used by permission of the publisher.

Ginn and Company for "Alexander Graham Bell" by Ernesto Ramírez. Adapted from Trail Blazers of American History, Revised Edition, by Miriam E. Mason and William H. Cartwright, © Copyright, 1966, 1961, by Ginn and Company (Xerox Corporation). Used by permission of the publisher.

Hamish Hamilton Limited, London, for "Sam" from The Trumpet of the Swan by E. B. White. Reprinted by permission of Hamish Hamilton Ltd.

Highlights for Children for "Rosa Bonheur," adapted from "Rosa Bonheur, 1822-1899" by Constance McAllister in Highlights for Children, February 1979. Copyright © 1979, Highlights for Children, Inc., Columbus, Ohio. Used by permission.

Margaret Hodges for "The Fire Bringer," adapted from her book The Fire Bringer. Published by Little, Brown and Co. Used by permission of the author.

International Creative Management for "The Steadfast Tin Soldier," adapted from Seven Tales by Hans Christian Andersen, translated by Eva LeGallienne. Reprinted by permission of Mitch Douglas, International Creative Management. Copyright © 1959, Eva LeGallienne.

Astrid Lindgren, Sweden, for "Pippi Finds a Spink," adapted from her book Pippi in the South Seas. Published by Viking Penguin Inc. Used by permission of the author.

Lothrop, Lee & Shepard Company for "What Good Is a Weed?" adapted from pp. 9-16 and 53-57 in What Good Is a Weed? by Robert H. Wright. Copyright © 1972 by Robert H. Wright. By permission of Lothrop, Lee & Shepard Company (A Division of William Morrow & Company).

Lutterworth Press, England, for "Prairie Winter," Parts 1 and 2, from The Long Winter by Laura Ingalls Wilder. Reprinted by permission of the British publisher.

Mondadori Publishing Company, Inc., for "Christopher Columbus," adapted from Christopher Columbus by Piero Ventura. Used by permission of the publisher and of Arnoldo Mondadori Editore, Verona, Italy.

William Morrow & Company, Inc., for "High Wind for Kansas," an adaptation of High Wind for Kansas by Mary Calhoun (without illustrations). Copyright © 1965 by Mary Calhoun. By permission of William Morrow & Company. Also for "Help!" from The Snopp on the Sidewalk and Other Poems by Jack Prelutsky. Text Copyright © 1976, 1977 by Jack Prelutsky. By permission of Greenwillow Books (A Division of William Morrow & Company).

The Saturday Evening Post Company for "The Phone Call" by Barbara Metzmeier. From Jack and Jill magazine, copyright © 1972 by The Saturday Evening Post Company, Indianapolis, Indiana. Adapted in play form from "The Phone Call" by Barbara Metzmeier.

Scholastic Magazines, Inc., for "The Crane Maiden," which is an adaptation of The Crane Maiden by Miyoko Matsutani. English text copyright © 1968 by Parents Magazine Press. Reprinted by permission of Four Winds Press, a division of Scholastic Inc.

Larry Sternig Literary Agency for "Squirrel in a What?" adapted from Chapter 5 of The Zoo Was My World by Wesley A. Young and Gloria D. Miklowitz. Copyright © 1969 by Dr. Wesley A. Young and Gloria D. Miklowitz. Reprinted by permission of Larry Sternig Literary Agency.

Toni Strassman for the poem "Your Own Best Secret Place" from Your Own Best Secret Place by Byrd Baylor. Text copyright 1979 by Byrd Baylor. First printed by Charles Scribner's Sons. By permission of Toni Strassman, Agent.

Illustrators and Photographers: Peter Bradford, cover, 8-9, 96-97, 170-171, 230-231, 296-297, 370-371; Gary Fujiwara, cover, 8-9, 96-97, 170-171, 230-231, 296-297, 370-371; Alan Mitelman, 1, 3-7, 38-41, 50-51, 62-63, 70-71, 94-95, 120-123, 140-143, 166-169, 188-189, 202-203, 226-229, 240-241, 248-249, 266-269, 292-295, 312-315, 338-341, 366-369, 388-389, 394-395, 416-417, 424-425; Linda Crockett-Hanzel, 10-21; Joan Landis, 22-29; Janis Schillinger, 42-49; Jos. A. Smith, 52-61; Michael L. Pateman, 64-69, 144-151; Jon Agee, 72-81; Sandy Rabinowitz, 82-93; Justine Strasberg, 98-99; Steven Alexander, 100-115; Stephen Ogilvy, 116-119; Adrienne Pearson, 124-131; B. F. Stahl, 132-139, 216-225; Jerry Pinkney, 152-159, 232-239; Kris Boyd, 160-165; Dave Niles, 172-179; Bernard LaCasse, 180-187; Sandy Schafer, 180-187; Michael Mariano, 190-201; Kyuzo Tsugami, 204-209, 342-357; Laszlo Kubinyi, 210-213; Patrick Blackwell, 214-215, 396-405; Terry Presnall, 242-247, 284-291; Harry Weese and Associates, 250-251; Freelance Photographer's Guild, 253; Clifford Timm, 256-265; The Granger Collection, New York, New York, 270-275; Dan Collins, 276-283; Diane Cole, 298-303; Jacqueline Chwast, 304-311; David Cain, 316-323, 337; Dora Leder, 328-336; Kyuzo Tsugami, 342-357; David McCall Johnston, 358-365; Claudia Fregosi, 372-380; Don Freeman, 381-387; The British Library, London, England, for reproduction permission for the signature of William Shakespeare, 387; Rudy Muller, 388; The Bettman Archive, 390; Cathy Bennett, 396-401; Lonnie Browning, 406-415; The Metropolitan Museum of Art, Gift of the Artist in Memory of Rosa Bonheur, 1922, for reproduction permission for the painting by Anna E. Klumpke, 418; The Trustees of The Wallace Collection, London, England for reproduction permission for the painting by Rosa Bonheur, 422; Manus Pinkwater, 426-453; William McDade, 454-477.

Design, Ginn Reading Program:
Creative Director: Peter Bradford
Art Director: Gary Fujiwara
Design Coordinator: Anne Todd
Design: Lorraine Johnson, Linda Post, Kevin Young, Cathy Bennett, Kristen Dietrich

478